SONGS OF WILD BIRDS

THE SOUND MIRROR.

Mounted on a tripod, the microphone is being focused.

SONGS

OF
WILD BIRDS

BY

ALBERT R. BRAND

Associate in Ornithology
American Museum of Natural History

THOMAS NELSON AND SONS

NEW YORK

1934

To my friend and teacher
PROFESSOR ARTHUR A. ALLEN
and those members
of Cornell University
both faculty and students
without whose constant help and encouragement
this work never would have been attempted,
I gratefully dedicate
this book

CONTENTS

SONGS OF WILD BIRDS

FOREWORD

It is a comparatively simple task to learn to recognize birds at sight, even those in obscure plumages; but to track down the voice in the tree tops, to hear the bird sing and then to identify the songster with certainty is a most time-consuming project, no matter how absorbing it may be.

Up to the present time there has been no short cut to this pleasant task. All my life I have been gradually learning the "language" of the birds, and for over twenty-five years endeavoring to teach it to my students at Cornell University. At times it has been a rather discouraging effort, for it is so difficult, not only to identify the songs, but to remember them from year to year, until one has heard them over and over again. Even the little phrases which we invent to help us remember the quality or the rhythm of the song are of little avail until after the song has been heard many times.

For years we awaited the invention of some method of mechanically recording the songs and calls of birds so that they could be taken back to the laboratory or the home and played over and over again so as to fix them in mind.

Finally, there came the talking picture, the sensitive microphone, the accurate recording of sound on film; and then came Albert Brand. Endowed with an unusual degree of patience and optimism and tenacity of purpose, he attacked the difficult problem—first at Cornell University—and then at the American Museum of Natural History, and this little book of bird songs is the first fruit of his labors.

As an ornithologist I commend it to you for the accuracy with which the songs have been recorded; as a teacher I recommend it as an easy method of learning and teaching to others the songs of our native birds; as an American citizen I hail it as saving for you the years of effort which I and hundreds of others have had to spend in learning the music of the birds. Each song learned makes all the rest so much easier to identify and to remember. Learn those on these records; recognize them when you hear them in field or forest—and you have ten years' start on those of us who had to figure them all out for ourselves. May they be, however, only the beginner's dictionary, in your very pleasant pursuit of translating the language of the birds into human experience.

May the voices of friends then greet you in every strange city; may familiar notes come to your ears wherever you may wander and, even in the wilderness, may you be aware of companions near you. This is the comforting thought that keeps recurring to me ever since I learned the songs and calls of our native birds, and I trust that with the aid of these records, this satisfaction may soon be yours as well.

Arthur A. Allen,
Professor of Ornithology,
Cornell University.

INTRODUCTION

It is probably true that more people are interested in birds than in any other wild creatures; and yet there are comparatively few who really know birds, or are able to identify more than a few of the commoner species. For, in order to know birds, it is practically essential to know their songs, and up to the present there has been no simple way of securing this knowledge.

It was with this thought in mind that the experiments that made this book possible were started, and it is hoped that the records which accompany the book will greatly simplify bird study. In the past the only way open for one who wanted to become even an amateur ornithologist was to spend a great deal of time afield, studying the birds in their natural habitat; and learning their songs by the long and tedious method of hearing them repeated many times. This usually took years. The result was that many really interested persons gave up. The job was too tedious, and it took too long even to begin to be proficient.

But with the aid of records of the actual singing bird, any one, whether he is musical or not, as long as he is not entirely tone deaf and in addition has no sense of rhythm whatever, any one who cares to devote a little time to it, can soon learn to identify not only birds that are generally thought to be common, but many others that we are told are rare and unusual. These birds are often not identified, because it is extremely difficult to know them, for one reason or another, unless their song is recognized. For when it sings, even the most secretive, mouselike bird gives away its identity.

I remember one particular case which happened at Ithaca while I was studying at Cornell University. The Henslow's Sparrow is an inconspicuous bird that lives in the grassy fields, nests on the ground, and rarely, even when singing, rises higher than a few feet. Its song perch is often a stalk of last year's goldenrod. This bird has a most inconspicuous song, but like practically all bird songs it is individual. That is, it has certain qualities, not difficult for the human ear to detect, that no other bird has. This sparrow was supposed to be a great rarity. What was actually the case was that very few of the bird students, among the comparatively many that study Ornithology at Cornell, knew Henslow's Sparrow. After we had learned the song, we found the bird to be quite common; in fact, there was hardly a time in May, June, or July, if you went strolling through the grassy fields, that you would not hear several Henslow's Sparrows.

This book is not a guide or handbook to birds generally. There are so many excellent works covering that field that it seemed unnecessary to describe again plumage, nesting habits, distribution, *etc.* There is, however, very little on song for the bird lover. It is hoped that this book may fill this gap in our nature library.

In identifying birds a knowledge of song is essential even to the most casual bird student. There are two essentials in bird study, the tools without which no one is able to make progress. They are the reading and writing of the subject—many will be glad to know there is no " 'rithmetic."

The first thing we must know is what the bird looks like; the second, is to recognize its song and calls. It is comparatively easy to get to know birds by eye. There are a number of beautiful bird pictures and plates that are available at reasonable prices. The three sets of Audubon Bird Cards are sold by the National Association of Audubon Societies, 1775 Broadway, New York City, for $1.00 a set. The states of New York and Massachusetts* have excellent plates of the birds seen in those states, which are sold to the public at or below cost. These sets are priced at something over a dollar a set, and are not only beautiful, but useful as well. So we are very well supplied if we want to learn what a bird looks like, and now, with bird songs recorded, we are able to study bird sounds so that we can use the knowledge thus acquired when we are out-of-doors.

One cannot hope to see all the birds that are present while in the field, for with many of them, at best, one can get but a fleeting glimpse, as they hasten away among the protective foliage. But with a knowledge of their songs and calls, many birds that the eye is unable to detect can be positively identified. I remember a census taken one May day recently. Fifty or more bird students took part, and over 150 species were identified; and probably half were heard and recognized that way, before they were seen. Many were never seen at all. My personal experience on this trip was that I first identified by ear over two-thirds of the birds I saw, and later verified the identifications by sight.

Most bird books and guides give a little about song either by using the musical scale, or by a syllabic interpretation of the song. Using musical notations is rarely successful; few birds sing in the conventional scale; and they seldom adhere in time or pitch to man-made musical standards. The second method, using syllabic interpretation, is extremely unsatisfactory, as there are few people who can understand this type of bird-song description. In fact, bird songs cannot be described adequately, any more than you can describe a glorious sunset. The late Edward H. Forbush, State Ornithologist of Massachusetts, says, "Attempts to suggest bird notes on paper almost always are inadequate. My own always have been unsatisfactory."

It was not until the perfection of radio amplification tubes—the basic invention that

* For New York plates write to the N. Y. State Museum, Albany, N. Y., and for those of Massachusetts to the Department of Agriculture, Commonwealth of Massachusetts, State House, Boston, Mass.

made the radio a reality—that it was at all possible to attempt to catch the songs of wild
birds.

The radio tubes with which we are now so familiar are not only the heart of the radio
set, but they are equally important in sound recording. Radio, sound motion pictures and
recording bird songs are all dependent on one element, the amplification tube. This is
why making phonograph records of bird songs has never been attempted before. It is only
with the aid of recently developed apparatus that bird songs can be faithfully recorded.

There has always been a demand for a better method of studying bird song; but it was
my good fortune to be the first person with the requisite time and sufficient interest to use
the "movietone" method in bird-song recording.

The addition of phonograph records as a tool for the study of bird song does not mean
that studying birds in the field will be supplanted. That will never happen—the field will
always be the best place to study wild life—but it does mean that another method of
learning is available, to supplement, rather than to supplant, the field-study method, and
henceforth it will not be necessary to spend so long a time afield, thus opening the gates
of bird lore to many a would-be student who, in the past, lacked time for this fascinating
study.

This book makes no attempt to be a complete repertory of bird song, nor are the accom-
panying records a complete set of all the songs of the eastern United States. It is the
author's hope and expectation to issue a second and possibly a third volume with sets of
records, and in time a complete set of songs for our territory will be available. This first
set of records contains thirty-five songs of birds, many of them among the commoner
species. It is hoped that they will be useful in teaching both adults and children, and that
they will be helpful to the teacher and to the lay student.

It never would have been possible to collect the songs recorded if it had not been for
the help and encouragement that the author received from a great number of people, so
many, in fact, that it is impossible to give them all credit here. This little book is too
small for me to mention each by name. However, I must acknowledge my grateful thanks
to Peter Paul Kellogg, instructor in ornithology, and M. Peter Keane, a student at the
University. Any time of day, or before daybreak, if need be, I was able to call on them.
They were always ready. Professor W. C. Ballard, Jr., Assistant Professor True McLean, and
Mr. Arthur Stallman, of the Engineering School, were ever ready to offer their advice,
as well as their active help with the complicated, technical, electrical machinery. Without
their skillful aid and knowledge little would have been accomplished.

Not only must one be an ornithologist to collect bird songs, but also something of a
physicist and electrical engineer. Whatever my claim may be as an ornithologist, I have
no claim to either of the other professions, and I would have made little or no progress
had it not been for the help of experts in these fields. The work was started as a piece

of research, while I was a student at Cornell University. It would not have been carried out had it not been for the constant help and encouragement of Professor Arthur A. Allen, to whom I owe a deep debt of gratitude. His students, associates, and fellow-professors, particularly those of the Electrical Engineering School, were always willing to help with the many difficult problems that arose in this first experiment of its kind. It was not an experiment of one individual, but of a whole department, aided, whenever necessary, by other departments in the University. It is, therefore, really to Cornell University, its faculty and students, that I owe my most grateful thanks.

CHAPTER I

RECORDING BIRD SONG

RECORDS of American song birds had never been made, and naturally, as we were treading on virgin soil, we had to move slowly. Two alternatives offered themselves; either the birds could be caught, caged, and if they could be coaxed to sing, their songs recorded; or the mechanism should be so built that it could be taken afield. Either the bird would have to be brought into the human habitation; or the human would have to go out into the bird's sphere.

Recording the caged wild bird appeared the simpler. There was only one drawback: most birds will not sing normally in captivity. Some will not sing at all; others, only in subdued and restrained tones; and a very few sing their normal song when taken out of their natural environment. One of these is the wild canary, the progenitor of our common caged bird. But this is the exception, not the rule. This single drawback was enough. To take bird-song records the bird must sing without restraint. The other alternative, going into the bird's environment, though fraught with many difficulties, turned out to be the practical plan.

The moving-picture industry has been quite successful in making newsreels, and these are taken out-of-doors, exactly as we intended to do. It is true newsreel films rarely have to record high-pitched sounds such as occur in bird song, but we felt that if the motion-picture industry could get sound in the open spaces, the naturalist ought to be able to do so too.

Scientific expeditions had lately gone out equipped with sound recorders, somewhat akin to the recording phonographs that have recently been perfected. It would be very simple to take that type of apparatus out into the woods, set it in place, and presto! you have your bird song. It did not occur to us that these machines are not very accurate, nor are they capable of reproducing high-pitched sounds of considerable delicacy; nor did we consider that in order to use them at all it is necessary to speak directly into the machine. One may not be less than six, nor more than twelve inches from the machine in order to get a good recording. It could hardly be expected that a wild bird would "step right up, and have your song recorded!"

We soon found this method was impractical, and that if bird sounds were to be gotten at all the sound-on-film method would have to be used. This is the method used by the motion-picture industry, and eventually an adaptation, more or less patterned after the newsreel location sound truck, was secured.

Our machine was, in essence, a specially designed and built, miniature edition of the sound half of just such a truck. No attempt was made to take motion pictures along with the sound, as that would have been so difficult and would have required so many operators as to make it impracticable. The motion-picture sound truck uses as many as five or six expert technical men to run it. Our machine was completely manned with a crew of two, neither of whom was a professional sound man; and not infrequently my assistant or I took the truck in the field unaccompanied, and returned with satisfactory recordings.

Photographing sound—for that is what the sound on film process actually is—is intricate and extremely delicate. It, like the radio and the telephone, is another of those marvels which modern science has wrought; and because man has become accustomed to them as commonplaces in his daily life, he accepts, without much thought, these twentieth-century miracles.

Our problem was somewhat different from the motion-picture industry's. We needed a machine sufficiently refined to photograph the extremely high sounds that birds make, and at the same time one that would not pick up too much of what are technically known as "ground noises." These are the sounds that are always present, but which our ears with the aid of our brain shut out from our consciousness. The ticking of a clock in our bedroom does not disturb our sleep—we say we become accustomed to it. Our brain does not transmit to us all the sounds which our ears pick up. But though man has been able to invent a mechanical ear—the microphone, and it is an extremely sensitive one, too—he has not been able to equip it with a brain. It transmits all the sounds it hears, without discrimination.

For sound recording in the open, therefore, as nearly absolute quiet as possible is essential. Another essential is that the machine should be extremely rugged, for it will have to withstand the strain of being taken into the field over good roads and bad, and sometimes, as it turned out, over no roads at all, but through the open country.

After numerous experiments and many heartbreaking failures, a machine was finally developed that was able to accomplish its purpose. This sound recorder was mounted in a small closed Ford delivery wagon. The apparatus consisted of two microphones, an amplifier, a sound camera, an impressive array of storage and dry-cell batteries, and several hundred feet of stout cable for connecting the microphone in the field to the rest of the recorder in the truck.

Sound consists of an intricate combination of regular vibrations which are given off by the sound source. The higher pitched the sound, the more frequent are the vibrations. The pendulum of a grandfather's clock makes one complete vibration each second. This, however, is of so low a frequency as to be inaudible. A deep bass voice can produce a note as low as sixty vibrations per second, while a high soprano can register up to about thirteen hundred per second. The human ear can detect sounds as low as twenty vibrations per second, and a person with acute hearing can distinguish sounds as high as fifteen thousand per second, and occasionally somewhat higher. The "movietone" method of recording consists of transforming the vibrations that affect the microphone first into electrical energy and then into light. The varying intensity of this light is then photographed on sensitized film.

Let us follow the course of the vibrations from the instant they strike the microphone until they have been photographed on the film. The microphone has been placed in the woods not far from the singing perch of a bird. When the bird sings he sends forth mechanical vibrations (sound). The microphone transforms these to corresponding electrical vibrations. These, however, are extremely small, and must be greatly magnified before we can use them. Our mechanical ear is designed to receive and amplify these small vibrations. This means that it increases their size, or multiplies them, let us say, one thousand or one hundred thousand times in power. After being amplified in the microphone, our transformed electrical vibrations travel through the cable to the amplifier in the truck. This amplifier has a familiar appearance, for it looks much like an ordinary radio; and no small wonder, as a radio is, at least in part, an amplifier. Here the vibrations are again magnified until they are finally so great that they can be transformed into sound, and heard through a pair of earphones. The person operating the sound camera in the truck wears these, and he can hear what is going on outside in the woods: a fly or a mosquito that may chance to get near the microphone can be heard distinctly more than two hundred feet away.

I recall early one morning having the microphone set up in the woods. I was in the car with all the windows and doors closed, and with earphones on. The mosquitoes were very thick that morning, and in the earphones I could distinctly hear their buzzing two hundred feet away. Not once, but half a dozen times, during the recording, I found myself slapping at the back of my neck, though I knew all the time that there were no mosquitoes in the truck.

But to get back to our sound wave, which has now been greatly magnified, and is ready to have its picture taken. From the amplifier it is conducted to a glowlamp. This also has a familiar look, for it seems to be an elongated electric-light bulb about an inch thick and eight inches long. We are now at the heart of the machine. It is here that the vibrations are converted into light. If you were to hold this bulb in your hand when the switches were on you would see, at the end of it, a peculiar ball of purplish light. This light would not be of constant brilliancy, but would flicker: one instant it would be most intense, the next, almost out; and this flicker would be continuous and extremely varied. What is really happening is that you are watching sound. Noises outside, near the microphone, are transmitted to the end of this glowtube, and the various vibrations that have been set up by the sound register as flickering light. It is these flickerings that are to be photographed. The glowtube is now fitted in a metal tube which leads into the light-tight compartment of the camera. There is, however, a small slit .001 of an inch wide, through which the light of the glowtube is allowed to shine. This slit corresponds to the lens in an ordinary camera.

The camera has a familiar look, also; it resembles a motion-picture camera. There is a magazine on top of it which has two compartments. The first of these carries the unexposed film, the second the exposed but undeveloped picture of the sound. When the motor switch is thrown, the unexposed film is carried into the camera. On its way to the second compartment, it travels directly in front of the light slit. The glowtube is on the outside of the slit, the fast-moving photographic film on the inside. As the film passes the slit the flickerings of the glowlamp are registered on its sensitized surface. Each second eighteen inches of film pass this slit in front of the flickering glowlamp. Thus the many flickerings, representing sound vibrations of various frequency, are faithfully photographed.

From this point the process is identical with motion-picture taking. The film is developed, and prints are made from the negative. It is then played on the same machine that is used in motion-picture houses.

People often ask how far away from the bird you can be and still get a good recording. The answer is that there is no specific distance. If you can hear a sound you can record it. However, it does depend somewhat on your apparatus, and a great deal on the carrying power of the particular sound. Thus in the recording of the Pied-billed Grebe, the bird was quite far out in the lake, but the Grebe's call is one that carries well, and there was the additional advantage of the sound coming across the water. In the case of the

Hermit Thrush on Record # 1B, we never even saw the bird, it was in the dense wood, and a light wind wafted the hymnlike chords right into our microphone. How far away the bird was, I have no way of telling. I do not think he was very far off, however, as the strains were loud and clear. He may have been fifty feet off, and perhaps he was somewhat nearer. While it is interesting to see the subject when sound recording, it is not essential; and in this instance, with a Hermit Thrush singing so gloriously, we can be excused if we made sure of our recording first, and later attempted to locate the songster. Some of the sparrows, the Long-billed Marsh Wren, and the Maryland Yellow-throat, were less than ten feet from the microphone when recorded.

A late development in our recording was the addition of a sound mirror, or parabolic reflector, to our equipment. This made it possible to record bird songs at much greater distances. The sound mirror is a large circular contraption, the shape of a parabola. The microphone is pointed toward the center of this disc, and in the opposite direction from the bird. With the use of this apparatus, the sound is magnified more than twenty times, before it enters the microphone. The reflector, with microphone attached, is set on a tripod. There is a sighting device—a primitive telescope—which is focused on the bird. The outstanding feature is that the mirror will only reflect sounds that are in focus with it. The song of the bird will be twenty or twenty-five times magnified, while all other sounds will remain as they were. Thus, in effect, the outside noises are very nearly shut out, while the sounds wanted are greatly increased. With this device we did some long-distance recording. Perhaps our longest shot of any of the common small birds was one of the Orchard Oriole. We were at least two hundred yards from the bird when this was taken, and the bird could hardly be distinguished through the telescope.

In order better to understand how these recordings are made, I am going to ask my reader to go with me on an imaginary early-morning recording. Birds are in full song for a comparatively short period of the year, and so most of the recording has to be done from mid-April to mid-July. About three-thirty of a fine cool morning in May our little truck rolls up before your door. The sun is not up yet but the sky is aglow with the glories of the coming day. The only sound is the morning chirp of an awakening Song Sparrow, or the occasional note of the early Robin, as he arouses himself to start his search for the proverbial worm. As we drive out through the dew-laden countryside toward the high woodland that is our destination, we pass a farmyard, and hear old chanticleer give his familiar refrain. This crowing of the rooster, pleasant as it sounds in the quiet of the morning, is likely to become a great nuisance, for his lusty cry has ruined many of our otherwise fine recordings.

We have now arrived at our woodland destination. I had been out here the day before, and looked over the ground to find the most likely place to set our microphone. A Northern Water-thrush has just started his bubbling warble. He repeats it constantly and at frequent intervals. It is so loud as to be somewhat startling. We are indeed fortunate, for here is a song that should record easily, and in the quiet of the early morning there are few interfering sounds.

I hop out, open the back door of the truck, and grab the end of a two-hundred-foot roll of cable. This is wound on a metal wheel which is on the door, and which unrolls as one walks out with it. I also sling a microphone, mounted on a tripod, over my shoulder.

It is set up in short order, within twenty-five feet of the low alder where the bird is singing; and very soon I am back in the truck with the earphones on, listening in. There are a few little details to attend to in the truck—tests to make to be sure that the batteries are at the correct amperage and voltage; the minute slit through which the exposure is to be made must be examined to see that no particle of dust is clogging it. The glowtube must be looked at, and then set in its place, next to the slit. However, with luck, we are ready to record in less than ten minutes. You, as my guest, sit next to me on the bench in the truck, opposite the camera. There is a spare set of earphones which you have on; you are amazed at how clearly you can hear the singing outside.

I listen for a minute or two, adjust several of the switches on the amplifier so as to get the correct volume in the earphones; and at the right moment, throw the motor switch which sends the film careening through the camera, merrily catching the gay gurglings of our ecstatic songster. The film is run for perhaps two minutes, and you have noticed that I have made adjustments from time to time. These, I explain, are changes in amplification. We increase or decrease the volume that is fed to the glowtube. Then after the film is developed we can pick out whichever song is the best. Not more than one-tenth of the film taken will be used, however.

But do not think that sound is always as easy to record as it was this morning. We have indeed been fortunate. Often we have started out under similar circumstances, only to find that ten minutes after the sun has risen, the wind has done the same. Our long trip to the location has been futile. It is not even worth while to take out the microphone. For wind is our worst bugbear. I never realized the meaning of such phrases as the whispering willows, and the mur-

muring pines, until I started sound recording. Even a moderate wind makes bird-song recording very difficult, if not impossible. Then frogs, too, can make great nuisances of themselves; we were fortunate that they did not start their raucous calls this morning, for, if they had, we never would have gotten our recording. The rooster I have already mentioned; his companions of the barnyard, the calf and the farmer's dog, can also make themselves extremely obnoxious.

In fact, there were several occasions when we had located birds singing that we were particularly anxious to record. All went well in setting up, until our operations were discovered by a neighboring watchdog. He expressed his disapproval of what we were doing in loud bursts of canine profanity. Even heaving rocks at him failed to have an effect for more than a few seconds. There was nothing to do except to shoot the dog, or pull up stakes and find a quieter location! Suffice it to say we went elsewhere. The farm tractor, too, can be very annoying; and other mechanical sounds, such as aeroplanes, or a train in the distant valley, will disturb the quiet of an otherwise excellent pastoral site. Too close proximity to a traffic road or to electric wires is fatal, so it can be easily seen that we had numerous obstacles besides the temperament of the birds themselves to hinder us.

And the birds! They were not always as good subjects as our Water-thrush. Time and again we would set up while a bird was singing beautifully, only to have him scared off by our maneuvers. Of course this is understandable, and not nearly so aggravating as such incidents as the following. Early one morning, we set up on a Catbird. He was in fine voice, and prospects were bright. Everything went smoothly during the set-up; it made my heart glad to hear his varied gurglings and splutterings, interspersed occasionally with his cat-like mew. But just as we had turned all the switches on, he stopped. The bird lice were bothering him. He gave up singing, and devoted himself to a search for the elusive insects. Thinking he would soon tire and resume his song, we let the machine run on. But no, he kept up the—shall we call it—"de-fleaing" process for a full two minutes. Meanwhile, our expensive film was placidly running through the camera at the rate of a foot and a half a second. Finally, I shut off the machine. This seemed to be our bird's cue, for he immediately started to sing again. He kept it up until we, thinking he was now certainly going to continue, switched on the machine a second time. How he got our signal I cannot say, but the perverse bird stopped before we had recorded a single chirp, and proceeded to scratch and dig once more. He was a most contrary bird, and if the truth must be told, we never did record that particular Catbird.

Bird-song recording sounds much simpler than it actually is. Getting up with the birds for months at a stretch may not be too disagreeable; in fact, the hour preceding dawn is one of the loveliest in the whole day; but it does cut into one's schedule considerably.

Then there are not only outside noises, both natural and mechanical, to contend with, but you have to deal with the extremely elusive and temperamental, though delightfully charming, bird itself. After many minutes, or hours, of patient waiting, you may finally get your bird. He is at his best, he pours forth a tumult of lusty song, and just as you start to record, some other songster which you had not noticed before starts his roundelay, quite drowning out the song of your original choice. When the second bird happens to be a Crow, and the first a Hermit Thrush, you can well imagine how disconcerting it is. A pretty record you will have with Crow in the foreground, and Hermit Thrush in the distance!

But the recording has now been made. The job is, however, only well begun. After developing the film, it must be played back, and later carefully edited. Playing back film can well be described as the reverse process of recording. The film is run through a machine known as a projector. This is the same machine which is used in the motion-picture houses to display sound movies.

Let us see how this reverse process works. Out in the field we were trying to get a picture of the sounds we were hearing; now we were trying to take the developed picture, and reconvert it into sound. The film running in the projector passes in front of a fine slit, exactly as it did in sound photography; but this time, instead of a glowtube to make an exposure, there is a photoelectric cell to pick up the photographed sound vibrations. The recently perfected photoelectric cell is one of the miracles of our wonderful era. It is extremely light-sensitive. A brilliant, carefully focused light shines on one side of the sound track through the fine slit and into the photoelectric cell on the other side. As the film passes the slit, the lines on the track—the photograph of the sound—are made to shine on the photoelectric cell, and the visible vibrations are again converted into electrical energy. As in the recording process, this energy is amplified or magnified, until finally it is great enough to be fed to a loud speaker which converts it from electrical energy into sound.

Editing is a never-ending task, for it is almost impossible to determine exactly where song is on the film, and it would not do to cut the bird's song in half, for instance. The safest method is the slow and tedious one of playing the film back, until by ear you have marked out the best cuttings. Ordinary low-frequency sounds such as the human voice or orchestral music are easily seen on the film, but not so with many of the extremely high bird sounds. For the higher pitched the sound, the closer together are the lines on the sound track, and the song of the Yellow Warbler, for example, appears on the film as a great number of very thin hair lines, so fine as to be hardly visible to the naked eye. They can best be seen under a magnifying glass in a strong light. Fortunate we are indeed that the photoelectric cell of the projector, that man-made "sound eye," has better than human vision, for had it not, we should never be able to reproduce the sound of wild birds.

Then, too, most of our film, for one reason or another, is not good enough to use for record making. If one-tenth of what we have taken in the field is usable we shall be well satisfied. But it is this tenth with which we are concerned. This is finally cut from the original film, spliced—which is the motion-picture industry's term for pasted together—and we are now ready to change our field of operation.

We are in the recording laboratory. Here the edited film is played through a sound recorder, and the electrically transformed sound, instead of being fed into a loud speaker as heretofore, is fed into the record cutter. The first record is made on a wax disc, and after various processes which it will not be necessary to describe here, but which are standard for making all phonograph records—after these various processes a finished record appears, and we have at last reached our goal.

At the break of day, in the wild bird's home, we have caught his song. We can now reproduce it with its original trills and cadences, at our leisure, in the confines of our living-room.

CHAPTER II

THE HOW AND WHY OF BIRD SONG

MANY a budding young naturalist gets his first thrill from the natural sciences through bird study. Though a student may, in later life, work in some other field of biology, surprisingly many start with class Aves. The reason is not hard to find. Bird's startling beauty, its interesting nesting habits, its solicitous care of the young, its command of the air through flight, its almost unbelievable migrations, in which it often returns year after year to the selfsame spot, and last, its song, which at its best exhibits beauty and variety far beyond the power of any other living creature—all these qualities appeal to man's imagination and call forth his wonder and amazement. It is not surprising, then, that since time immemorial man has woven the bird theme into his folk lore, poetry, fable, and symbolism; and into his music he has incorporated snatches of bird song.

Of all bird's startling activities, song is one of the most alluring. Other creatures make sounds, some, such as the crickets, of a high musical order, but none can compare in variety or beauty to bird song.

One would suppose, with this interest in birds and their singing, that down through the ages a vast store of knowledge of bird song would have been gathered. Unfortunately, this is not the case. Bird song, though beautiful to listen to, is extremely difficult to study. For birds are elusive creatures. Few thrive in captivity; practically none behaves normally in that state; so that almost any knowledge of song has to be acquired by studying birds in the wild state. Who has not learned at a very early age how difficult this is? The toddling three-year-old, trying to put salt on the "birdie's" tail— is he not, at that tender age, taking his first lesson in the elusiveness of our feathered neighbors? Bird's structure, its mating habits, its diet, and lately, even its awe-inspiring migrations, have been the subject of careful scientific study, and while there are many facts on these and kindred topics that are still unknown, yet a considerable amount of knowledge has been amassed.

It is different with song. Here we are dealing almost entirely with theories and speculation. Many of the guesses sound logical, some few are backed by careful observations and experimentation, but it is very difficult to be definite and specific. There are too many theories and too few facts. So if my reader finds that what I have to say is incomplete, or only partly satisfactory, he will remember that the fault is not entirely mine, but that we are discussing a subject about which we have very little definite knowledge.

Not all birds sing, though most of them make some kind of sound. For convenience, bird sounds can be roughly divided into two groups: calls, and songs. Aretus A. Saunders, in "Bird Song," defines song as "a vocal performance usually confined to the male, and to a definite season including the time of courtship"! He goes on to explain that song "is not necessarily musical, and in fact in some species, such as the Grackle and the Yellow-headed Blackbird, it is distinctly harsh and nonmelodious to the human ear. The crow of a rooster may properly be considered a song, but one is not likely to be impressed with its musical beauty. The twitter of a flock of Tree Sparrows feeding in the weed tops above the snow on a winter day is extremely musical and pleasing, but is not properly song."

"The term call notes is somewhat loosely applied to a great variety of bird utterances, including true *call* notes as well as notes or 'calls' of alarm, anger, *etc.*" (F. M. Chapman). In addition to these there are other bird sounds which are not the product of the voice box. Some of them, such as the drumming of Grouse and the tattooing of Woodpeckers, are part of the courtship performances, and can be considered as substitutes for song.

The development of the vocal organs in birds is peculiar. Whereas in mammals the vocal cords are in the larynx, at the top of the windpipe, in birds they are situated in a special song-box, the syrinx, at the base of the windpipe. This special organ is found in no other class of animals. Birds, like mammals, have a larynx, at the upper end of the windpipe, but its structure is simpler. In mammals it contains the vocal cords; in birds these are found in the true song-box, the syrinx, and the larynx and tongue merely modify the sound produced lower in the body. If you watch a bird sing, you will notice the motion is far down in the throat. In fact, it appears to originate in his breast. In the true singing birds, called oscines, the song-box is more specialized than in other birds, and these oscine birds are considered the most advanced group. Most of our song birds are in this group, but there are many species among the lower birds—those with simpler song-boxes—with elaborate and interesting songs, while among the oscines are such birds as the Crows, Bluejays, and House Sparrows—birds whose vocal organs are of the highest type but whose voices, nevertheless, are decidedly commonplace and unlovely.

Though no two birds of the same species—no two Robins, for instance—sing exactly alike, their voices are so similar and the differences are so slight that they can be readily identified. In addition,

LISTENING IN.

The sound apparatus in action. With ear phones on, the operator in the truck watches the monitor board to see that the bird song is recorded properly.

each species' song is distinctive. Aretus A. Saunders says of this phenomenon: "One of the first facts the student of birds who pays some attention to songs notices is that each species of bird has a distinctive song. Once the song of the species is known, any bird of that species that sings in a normal manner may be identified as readily by its song as by its plumage. Thus this specific difference in song is of great value to the field ornithologist." We can expect to learn little about birds unless we are familiar with their songs, and with the aid of phonograph records learning the songs of the individual species should be very much simpler than heretofore.

Sometimes birds of different species have similar songs—this is true particularly of birds whose songs are comparatively simple—but there is always some slight difference which is constant in the species, and which makes it possible for the careful student to identify the birds correctly. Thus the common songs of the Chipping Sparrow, the Swamp Sparrow, the Pine Warbler, the Junco and the Worm-eating Warbler are very much alike; and all can be described as a string of dry chips; yet there are differences between each of these songs which the experienced student can detect.

Closely related birds often have songs that are quite similar though usually easily distinguished from each other. Thus the thrushes of the genus *Hylocichla*, which includes the Wood Thrush, Hermit Thrush, Veery or Wilson's Thrush, and Olive-backed Thrush, have songs which are considerably alike. They are, however, easily distinguished, as each song has its individual quality. Listen to the record of these thrushes (# 1B) and you will see that all are decidedly different, though each suggests the others.

Certain vireos—the Red-eyed, Yellow-throated and Blue-headed —show their relationship in their songs. The Red-eyed's song is strident, rather quick, and sounds as if the bird were in a hurry, and must get the song out of his system. The Yellow-throated sings more leisurely, it is more reedy, and usually louder than the Red-eyed. The Blue-headed is the sweetest singer of the three; his song is much like the Red-eyed's but is louder, clearer, more musical, and more deliberate. Often it is not easy to separate these three—I had considerable trouble until I had heard them all singing a number of times—but with the aid of records and after a little study, one ought soon to be able to tell them apart. We can therefore safely say that each species of bird sings a song peculiar to his species, and that it is not an insurmountable task to learn to recognize the different songs.

But birds are individuals as well as members of species; and each individual bird interprets his song in his own way. Just as you most certainly would recognize a human voice if you heard it in the next room and would not confuse it with that of any other mammal, so, too, can you recognize a Robin's voice, and know that it is not a Scarlet Tanager that is singing. But just as individuals have differences in their voices, so, too, have birds. The mother's voice is not the same as the teacher's, and the ear has learned to distinguish the difference. This may seem to add more difficulties to identifying birds by ear, but in practice it does not, because birds of the same species sing so like members of their own species that they are easily recognized.

After you have become more or less familiar with bird songs, you will find that the same bird may visit your grounds for several years. You will recognize their peculiar interpretation of their racial song. Thus I know that a certain Song Sparrow spent all of last winter in my garden. I heard him last fall, again during the winter, and from January twenty-fifth on he sang until well into the summer. I knew it was the same bird because of the peculiarities of his song. It was most certainly a Song Sparrow's song—that any novice could tell; but it also was an individual song, the song of this particular bird. He had a certain way of delivering his song, using certain phrases that no other Song Sparrow I have heard uses.

It is very probable that birds of the same species which nest in different localities develop slightly different songs, just as people living in Georgia speak a slightly different English from those living in Massachusetts. Such differences have often been noted by bird students, and in my sound-recording trips I have noticed them, also. Thus the Song Sparrows of the New York Finger Lake district have a decided Finger Lake accent, when compared with the birds of the Hudson River district; and I have observed the same phenomenon in the songs of the Maryland Yellow-throat.

Bird songs are infinitely varied. This variety makes the study increasingly fascinating, even if it does not simplify. As I said before, there is a certain something about the song of a particular species that makes one recognize it. What that something is is difficult or impossible to describe. That is one reason why bird-song records ought to be extremely useful.

Not only do birds' songs vary as to species and as to individuals, but at different times in the year the song of the same bird will vary. Bird song is seasonal at best, and while birds utter sounds (call notes of various kinds) whenever they are present, song is at its height only during the comparatively short breeding season. This does not mean that birds never sing except at this time. Many birds sing before they have reached the breeding grounds, and there is also a period after the breeding season in which there is a moderate resumption of song. It is quite usual that as the season progresses, song becomes more elaborate, although the bird does not sing as often as in the springtime. Some of the late summer and fall offerings are among the most beautiful, though at this season they are much softer and more subdued than earlier in the year.

Each species has its own song habits. Thus the thrushes are rarely heard in migration; even the Robin, which, by the way, is a thrush, is silent for a week or two after his early arrival; and it is not until April that we are likely to hear his cheery song. On the other hand, the warblers sing as they travel, and even those that nest far north of us allow us to hear their pleasant voices.

In the late winter, some birds, which are merely winter visitants in our territory, start to sing. A few individuals of the flock of Tree Sparrows that spent the winter foraging in our stubble fields and hedges now burst into real song. All winter long we have enjoyed their musical twitterings as they called to one another, but this was not song, merely call notes; now, however, their performance is quite different, and they are rehearsing the song they are going to use, some weeks hence, on their breeding grounds in Labrador. Some bird voices we hear all through the summer, others, such as the Baltimore Oriole and Bobolink, sing only for a comparatively short period, a month or so, and then gradually stop. Hearing Bobolinks after early July is a rarity, and the Oriole, if he still is in song at that time, very much abbreviates his offerings.

Then, too, a number of birds are not satisfied with one song and variations of that song, but must have two or even more; one entirely different from the other. This may be confusing to the beginner, but he need not worry unduly as it is not too common a performance; and most birds sing one of their variations almost exclusively, and save the second for very special occasions. Several of the warblers—the Chestnut-sided, Blackburnian, and Ovenbird—and some sparrows, have this two-song habit. Then, too, there are variations due to age. It is believed that a young bird does not sing his traditional song as well as his elders; he has not had so long a time to practice it. And lastly, in the almost endless list of bird-song variations, are the abnormal songs. These we have to admit are disconcerting; but they add to the sport of bird stalking. Perhaps you chase for half an hour, as I did this summer, the originator of a song, cheerful and lovely, that you have never heard before. It reminds you of many things you have heard, but is identical with none. At the end of the chase you discover that you have heard a Scarlet Tanager—it did somewhat suggest a Tanager but it might have been a Robin or a Rose-breasted Grosbeak—and you get a feeling of satisfaction and joy at having discovered the perpetrator of this new and lovely sound.

Many birds are fond of mimicking their neighbors, and some are quite skillful at the art; but almost all the mimics sooner or later give away their identity by adding a few of their own notes. The Mockingbird and his relatives, the Brown Thrasher and the Catbird, have a particular weakness for this type of diversion. I well remember a Catbird that imitated a Whip-poor-will so cleverly that it would have been difficult to tell them apart, had he not, every now and then, interlarded a few of his catlike mews. Starlings also are excellent imitators, as are Blue Jays and many other species.

Just as birds have a special time of year for their singing so there are certain times of day more favorable to song than others. We all know how in May and June there is a veritable galaxy of song about the hour of sunrise. The reason that most of the records that accompany this book were gotten in the early morning is that song is most abundant at that time. About three-quarters of the songs were recorded before seven-thirty A.M. Another good time is just before dusk. During the heat of the day, birds are likely to be quieter.

Then, too, for some obscure reason, certain days seem more favorable for song than others. Just why this is, we do not know, and this subject offers an excellent opportunity for some student who would like to make a contribution to science. Still, cool days are generally best. Very hot, sticky weather, or a day when the wind is high, is generally poor, but there are times when conditions would seem ideal, and you can hear very little song, and others when wind and weather seem adverse, yet you will be treated to a continuous concert.

Not all birds have the same manner of singing. Some birds sing from the tops of tall trees; others prefer telegraph wires; still others find perches on stubble or low bushes, some, such as the famous Skylark of Europe, sing almost entirely on the wing; and quite a number occasionally sing while on the ground.

There are also different types of bird song. Some, like the Robin, sing in long-continued phrases, others, like most of our sparrows and a good many warblers, repeat at short intervals the same phrase. Such are the song of the Field Sparrow and Yellow Warbler. Then there are birds like the vireos which have a halting succession of phrases, four or five, perhaps, and which, after they have seemingly finished the roundelay, keep right on. They start anywhere in the cycle, and end at no particular point: there is everything from the modest chirps of the House Sparrow, to the elaborate warblings of the Purple Finch and Winter Wren.

The variations are infinite, some birds even singing at night. Of course there are our nocturnal singers, the Owls, Night Hawks, and Whip-poor-wills, which rest during the day; but there are also occasional night singers, birds that normally are diurnal in their habits. The Mockingbird of our southern states is said to be a regular singer on moonlight nights, and sings as fully and vivaciously as in the daytime. The European Nightingale is also reputed to be partial to moonlight. Almost any species is likely to sing occasionally at night during the height of the mating season. I can recall hearing Song Sparrows and Savannah Sparrows singing well into the night, long after these birds were supposed to be fast asleep.

We now come to the question, why do birds sing? Of what use is their song, and has it a purpose? Of course we need not limit our discussion to song alone, but shall include, as well, all other bird sounds. No one who has heard a Robin scold as he approached the nest can doubt that the anger call has meaning; and that it is quite different from the meaning of the call that the same Robin makes when, leading his immature offspring on the lawn, he finds them a particularly luscious worm. Dr. A. A. Allen, in "The Book of Bird Life," says, "There can be little doubt that the voice in birds has been developed, as in other animals, as a means of communication." The function of call is to make the bird heard by others of its kind; it is its language. It may not be, and probably is not, so highly developed as in human beings, but it undoubtedly is sufficient to serve the bird's needs.

The natural inference is that a bird sings to attract his mate. The fact that the male is the singer, and only rarely does the female indulge in song, seems to confirm this. And it is true that birds undoubtedly do attract their mates by their song; but it is believed today that this is rather a secondary use of song. Recent studies by H. E. Howard, a British ornithologist, indicate that the main purpose of song is something other than getting the parent birds together. Mr. Howard expounded what is known as the "Territory Theory." A. A. Saunders, in "Bird Song," gives the following brief résumé of this theory. "Each male bird, when it arrives in spring at the region where it will remain for the summer, mate and nest, selects a general area on which it lives, centering about the place where it sings habitually day after day, its singing tree or headquarters. The bird from the time of selection of its territory keeps other males of its species away from the spot. Its song, ringing out from headquarters, warns other males of its species to keep away, and thus avoids much fighting that might otherwise result." This theory explains many mysteries that we otherwise would not understand.

Territory varies greatly with different species, depending largely on differing food habits. Thus hawks, or eagles which hunt over a large territory, rarely if ever nest close to each other; the Belted Kingfisher usually patrols the stream for a half mile on either side of the bank where he has dug his nesting hole. If any male Kingfisher—and after mating has taken place, any female—should enter the sacred precinct, there is almost sure to be a furious fight. One or the other will have to surrender.

While the Kingfisher demands his mile of fishing grounds—his territory—many birds are content with much less; thus there may very well be two or three pairs of Catbirds and Robins in a garden of less than an acre; and some birds even nest in colonies. Many swallows, for example, build their nests side by side; yet, though it is very small indeed, each has his own territory which is respected by his brothers. Just as with man, his home is his castle, so with the bird, his territory is his citadel, and woe betide the intruder! We must bear in mind that the invading bird must be one of his own species; most birds do not object to neighbors, if they are not of their own kind. So when you go into the garden you may well find a Chipping Sparrow, Robin and Baltimore Oriole inhabiting the same tree; but you will rarely if ever find two pairs of Baltimore Orioles or two pairs of Robins nesting side by side.

It is fairly safe to say that the most important function of song is its use in defending the territory. It is the territory stimulus that makes the bird choose a singing perch. Many birds have this habit. They pick one particular spot on a particular limb. Here they return day after day, and hour after hour, sending forth a challenge to the rest of their kind, to keep off, or take the consequences.

This habit I found very useful when I was recording. If I could discover a "singing tree," I could come back to the spot at some later time, with my sound camera, and very probably I would get my recording.

We can therefore say that first in importance in bird song is the establishing of territory, and then, more or less incidentally, attracting the female. And here is another interesting phase. The female, though made conscious of the presence of the male by his song, is at first more interested in his territory than she is in him. Upon arrival she takes little or no heed of her future mate, though he showers his attentions on her, and displays in his best manner the beauties of his brilliant plumage. Like the matter-of-fact little creature that she is, she looks over his territory. If she does not approve, she moves on. If, however, this is just the place she has been looking for, she accepts the territory, and incidentally, of course, its owner. Then she proceeds to select a particular spot to build the nest in, while he mounts his singing perch, and defends the territory. In May and June you will notice much of this territorial activity. Last spring near my camp for a whole day there were a couple of male Indigo Buntings engaging in what appeared to be a duel unto death. Two birds had selected the same territory. They fought and sang incessantly, singing often on the wing, while chasing or being chased. Undoubtedly one was the victor, but the loser did not suffer much, for though the fight was very vigorous and extremely noisy, it was probably a case of "barking dogs never bite," and these fights rarely end in casualties.

Bird song is believed to have an additional use, in teaching the young birds their ancestral carol. It is not known whether song is inherited or learned, although much theorizing has been done on this subject. Most authorities seem to feel that while calls are inherited, song is at least partly a matter of environment. If the young bird is to learn his patriarchal song he has to do it from hearing his father, for he will not sing, it is generally believed, until the nesting season following his birth, at the earliest; and at that time, if he is to be recognized by his future mate, he must be able to sing the racial song.

Calls and bird sounds generally have their uses, also, in keeping birds together. Migrating flocks have often been noted where the individuals were calling, one to the other. In fact such flocks travelling at night are often quite noisy. On these journeys, which cover hundreds and sometimes thousands of miles, these location calls must be extremely useful. Our winter residents, Juncos, Tree Sparrows, Snow Buntings, *etc.*, keep together in more or less compact flocks, by responding to each other's calls.

Finally, there is an endless variety of special calls, the meaning of many being quite obscure to human observers; but it is obvious from the method in which they are delivered that they have a very special meaning and are readily understood by the feathered tribe. Some of these that we humans are able to interpret are the hunger cry of the young, danger calls, and calls to brood.

How did bird sound first come about? Birds' closest relatives are reptiles, and scientists believe that birds sprang from a primitive type of reptile, the pseudosuchians, or false crocodiles. "That the immediate ancestors of birds, as a class, were reptiles is about as nearly proved as is the ancestry of any single class of animals. Reptiles, however, are usually silent creatures, seldom producing sounds" (A. A. Saunders). But while reptiles are ground-inhabiting animals, of more or less sedentary habits, birds live in trees and in the air, and many of them cover many miles each day, while on their search for food, not to mention their long migrations taken twice a year. A flying animal can well afford to be noisier than a terrestrial one, for it can escape danger more rapidly than a non-flier.

It is believed that bird sounds originated in call notes, and that gradually, as birds developed and their needs changed these call notes were varied and improved upon, and that finally they became so transformed as to be the basis of what we know as song. We shall have to admit that at this point our definite knowledge is very hazy. It had better be called speculation, for the proofs of these assumptions are difficult to discover. But that song is often made up largely of the call notes of a species, that it is a series of variations of those call notes, is often quite evident, and makes the theory plausible.

In addition, some of our birds' songs appear to be in a state of evolution or change, and suggest that they are developing from simple calls to more elaborate songs. The House Sparrow, for example, has a song, though you may find it difficult to recognize. It is very similar to the call which we hear so commonly in the winter: but at the approach of spring the male's call becomes slightly more elaborate—a trifle more song-like. The same thing has been noticed in Crows and Blue Jays. Their raucous calls are embroidered a bit as the nesting season approaches, and it is possible to detect a song in the making.

The value to the bird student of recognizing bird sounds has already been pointed out, but here are a few little tricks that will be useful to any one interested in the subject. If one is a fair whistler there are a number of bird calls and songs that are not hard to imitate; and birds are easily fooled. I, myself, am no expert whistler, but have no trouble in imitating quite a few songs. The "Pewee" call of the Chickadee can be imitated by almost any one; and the bird responds to it very well. As Chickadees have a habit, in all but the mating season, of traveling in association with a number of other species of smaller birds, you often get a chance to see quite a variety of birds when you call the Chickadee. The White-throated Sparrow's song is also easily imitated, as is the Bob-white's. And I have even called the Red-shouldered Hawk from out of his forest haunts with what appeared to me a mediocre imitation of his eery cry.

Another ruse which often works, particularly during the breeding season and shortly thereafter, when young birds are recently out of the nest, is the "squeak." This is accomplished by imitating the distress call—a call that seems to be understood by all species. The imitation is produced by moistening the back of the hand, and kissing it. It is usually well to keep the lips fairly wet also. The

resulting sound suggests the noise a young bird makes when in
trouble, and the trick is often successful in bringing many species
within observation. It takes a little time to learn, but it is really
quite simple, after a little practice. If you remain hidden, after a
little successful squeaking, you may be able to get a close view of
ten or twelve different species. In my experience birds are more
sensitive to motion than to noise—that is, they are more easily
frightened off by a person moving in the bushes or woodland than
by their conversing. So when you employ the "squeak" it would
be well to stand still, preferably more or less hidden, or at least
appearing as inconspicuous as possible. It does not pay to keep up
squeaking indefinitely, however. Birds are readily adaptable, and
while at first your squeak may cause a great hubbub of excitement,
after a short time the birds get used to it, and then will pay it scant
attention.

CHAPTER III

HOW TO USE THE BOOK

This book is not a scientific treatise on bird song, but a practical work which it is hoped will be frequently used and constantly consulted. It has been my endeavor throughout, and especially in the text that follows, to make it as simple and as useful as possible. I have not hesitated to use any material that I felt would aid the earnest student. It is hoped that when a bird lover returns from the field after having heard a song with which he is not familiar, by playing the records, and with the aid of the text, he will be able, in many cases, to know to what bird he has been listening. In winter, when there are few birds around, he can familiarize himself with the various songs and calls by playing the phonograph records, and he will more readily identify the birds when they arrive in spring.

The records are by far the most important part of the work. The text is merely an auxiliary by which it is hoped the difficulties of identification will be clarified. It is as a check-up that it is expected to be most useful.

Customarily, bird books follow a definite order in the presentation of the material; and while this is an excellent scheme for most works, in this particular one it seems inadvisable to follow the usual order of relationship, but instead to have the birds arranged in groups according to the similarity of their songs. This is done for practical reasons; for it will be much easier for the user if he can hear the songs of confusing species while hunting for the one he has heard in the field. In this way he can learn the various peculiarities that make each individual species' song recognizable.

Each record contains eight or nine songs on each side, and although we have not always been able to arrange all the songs in this way, it has been done in this manner whenever possible. In some instances nearly related species are in close proximity to each other. Thus the Catbird, the Brown Thrasher, and the Mockingbird—all members of the same family—are on the same record. In the cases of the Robin, the Scarlet Tanager, and the Rose-breasted Grosbeak, you will find them on one record, though they are not closely related, each belonging to a different family. Their songs, however, are sufficiently alike to confuse a beginner, and it was for this reason that the record was arranged in this way.

One cannot identify birds by being proficient in one particular branch of bird knowledge alone, and being ignorant in others. That is one reason why so many people have found bird identification difficult in the past; and why few have become really proficient. Knowing birds by sight is not enough; one must also recognize the songs and calls. Now that electrical methods of recording sound have come to our aid, learning to do that will be much simpler, and it will not be an insurmountable task to recognize by sound as well as by sight. But even with both these accomplishments there are other things to know before one can become expert.

Birds have various habits that sometimes give them away more readily than their sounds and their feathering. Thus, one should not expect to find a Maryland Yellow-throat hopping around in the topmost branches of a tall tree—he is a bird of the tangled shrubbery, and one almost invariably finds him near the ground. Goldfinches and woodpeckers have peculiar habits of flight that are

quite diagnostic. Their flight is wavy or undulating. The time of
year is also an aid in identification. One is not likely to see a Barn
Swallow or a Chipping Sparrow in mid-winter: the bird that looks
like a Chipping Sparrow at this season is almost sure to be a Tree
Sparrow. Then, also, where you see the bird is helpful. You will
not find Meadowlarks in dense woods, or Ovenbirds in the open
fields. The more knowledge of this kind the student has, the better;
and sometimes it is only by a combination of all the facts that one
is able to make a correct identification. For that reason I have added
in the text a short paragraph headed "Notes," in which I have tried
to give a few of the most salient characteristics.

The text has been made as concise as possible; and the available
information has been gathered about the song of each bird recorded.
In the first heading, "Approximate dates when song is abundant,"
no attempt is made to be strictly accurate. In the first place that is
rarely possible. Birds are individuals, and vary as individuals will.
Song is linked up with the annual cycle of physiological or bodily
change through which the bird passes. The various molts and the
instinct to migrate are also connected with these changes; and rarely
are two birds affected by them in exactly the same manner, or at
more than approximately the same time. The dates chosen are, in
general, those during which song is most likely to be abundant
around New York City. This district has been chosen mainly because
it is fairly central for the area that the work attempts to cover. For
birds that are not present, or are very rare around New York City,
I have used dates at centers where the birds are common.

The paragraph on "location when singing" attempts to give the
observer some idea where he may expect to find the songster. Birds
vary in singing habits as generally as they do in their other activi-

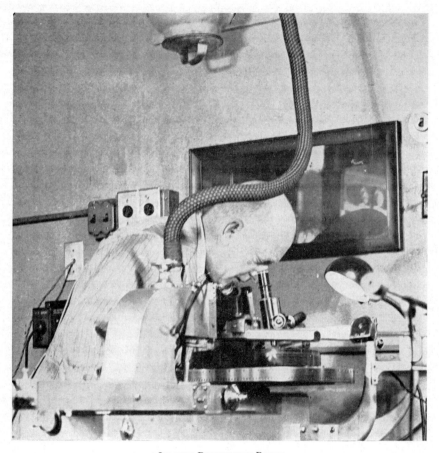

IN THE RECORDING ROOM.

Transferring the sound on film to a wax disk from which the phonograph records are eventually made.

ties. Some, like the Scarlet Tanager, often sing from the tops of trees; others, like the White-throated Sparrow, prefer low bushes; still others—the Grasshopper Sparrow, for example—usually take song perches not more than two or three feet from the ground, and that particular bird often selects some tall weed or low post, and sometimes sends forth his insect-like song from the very ground. Horned Larks, Bobolinks and Goldfinches and many others sing while in flight. During the height of the season, however, birds may sing in unusual places. In trying to record the song of a Grasshopper Sparrow, one morning in June, I chased the bird for several hours around a five-acre field, trying to get him to land on a post where he had first been seen singing. The microphone which had been set up a few feet away from the post proved to be too much for our intended subject, however. He would fly to the song perch, hover over it for a few instants, but could not get up courage enough to land. Still he had to sing, so he would go to any other available spot in the field, though the post was undoubtedly his favorite song perch. I was persistent, and chased him off, every time he landed. Finally he grew tired of being badgered, and flew up to the very topmost branch of a high elm, and there proceeded to get the song out of his system. I have seen other Grasshopper Sparrows sing on perches that were unusual for their species. In Virginia recently, one sang daily while perched on a telegraph wire. I cite this example merely to show that birds will not always follow their own rules. There are often exceptions and variations: these do not make bird study simpler, but they do make it vastly more fascinating.

In the paragraph on "Song" and the one on "Calls" an attempt is made to give in print a suggestion of what bird sounds are like. These notations are, I feel, of doubtful value, but I give them because they may be of some aid, particularly to a person who is partially familiar with a song, and wants to check up. Making verbal descriptions of bird songs is a sorry task. Many bird songs, in their variety and beauty, are indescribable. Trying to describe the indescribable is bound to result in disaster!

"Catch phrases," I also feel, are not wholly satisfactory; but because they may be useful to some students, I include them. Some I have found helpful in my own field work, particularly after I have begun to become familiar with a song. They have a way of setting it in your mind, giving you something concrete to call upon when you want to remember an otherwise too easily forgotten song. Individuals often differ in what they hear a bird sing; and some find it convenient to make up words of their own to interpret what they have heard. The "Poor-Sam-Peabody, Peabody, Peabody," of the White-throated Sparrow I have always found quite easy to pick out; but in Canada, where the bird is common, it is said to sing "Sweet Canada, Canada, Canada," and these words fit quite as well as the "Peabody" refrain. "Drink your Tea," as the song of the Towhee, satisfies me; but I have heard it quoted as "Hot-dog, Pickle-ickle-ickle," and "Holy Gee!" Catch phrases may be useful; they are set down here for what they are worth; I personally feel the student will get much more out of playing and replaying the actual records of the songs.

In the paragraph headed "Notes," I have attempted to give a few of the most characteristic mannerisms of the birds, particularly with reference to their songs and calls. These make no pretense of being complete—that would necessitate a much larger and an entirely different type of book—but I have set down a few observations which I felt would be most helpful to one who was attempting to master a knowledge of bird song.

On the records I have let the birds speak for themselves; and generally there is merely an announcement before the song of what bird is doing the singing. There were several reasons for this; but the main one is that the student can get all the information he wants about the bird from the written word, and as there is only a limited amount of space on the records, it seemed wasteful to use it for human talk. What we really want to learn is bird songs; the records, therefore, are entirely devoted to them. As a rule the song given on the record is the commonest one of the bird, and wherever possible an example of the most usual call note is added. The reader will understand that to record all the sounds of even one bird is practically impossible, and numerous secondary calls and songs which I would like to present are not here, often because we have never recorded them. However, it will be found that the commonest, most diagnostic song or call on the records will give the student a sufficient idea of the bird's singing, so that the more unusual sounds can be readily picked up.

When playing the records it will be found that the better the phonograph the truer and more lifelike will be the reproduction. Satisfactory results, especially for one who wants to learn, can be gotten from any phonograph that will run, but often the finer shadings and the quality will be lacking in some songs if the phonograph is incapable of taking the higher frequencies. Just as a fine pianist cannot produce as good music on a cheap dance-hall piano as he can on a concert grand, so you must not expect to get the same results from a second-hand ten-year-old mechanical phonograph that you will get from a fine orthophonic or electrically amplified modern machine. One more word of caution: with sound, the room in which the sound is produced will often affect it, sometimes causing distortions, and sometimes affecting the volume. This will be found particularly true in large auditoriums. Some will be quite satisfactory, others will be more difficult. Then, too, sounds of birds indoors are at best a bit artificial; you are used to hearing birds sing in the open, and our hearing is always more or less tempered by our mental processes. For instance, in one of our first experiments, we were working on our bird songs in a cellar: it did not sound natural, and we could not understand why. Finally an expert in acoustics suggested that we set the loud speaker on the lawn just outside the cellar window. This we did, and the improvement was astonishing. In fact, a Robin who happened to be de-worming the lawn at that moment became quite perturbed about the competition of the loud speaker's Robin, and flew around in great excitement in search of his rival.

Using the records in conjunction with pictures has been found to work very well, as this creates an atmosphere of naturalness, which aids greatly in classroom work. Slides of birds can be used, if they are available, and if one has a lantern slide projector. If equipment and slides are lacking home-made equipment can be substituted. My two sons, aged eleven and thirteen, rigged up a projector out of a wooden box, a couple of tin cans, a little black paint, an electric light bulb and an old lens. Most of the material was found around the house, and the total cost was under ninety cents. The Audubon Bird Cards were then projected on a sheet while the records were being played, and the illusion was very satisfactory. I mention this incident because it may be of value to teachers when using the records. It would not be difficult for a class of children to make for themselves, at very nominal cost, their own sound pictures.

DESCRIPTIONS OF BIRDS

SONG SPARROW

Melospiza melodia melodia (Wilson)

Other names: Eastern Song Sparrow, Ground-bird, Ground-sparrow.

Record # 1A

Approximate dates when song is abundant: Late March until late July. These are the dates when song is most abundant, but Song Sparrow songs are heard in the vicinity of New York City in every month of the year.

Usual location when singing: From the topmost twig of bush or low tree, often near man's abode but never far from water and thicket.

Song: "A voluble and uninterrupted but short refrain" (E. T. Seton), extremely variable. "Bright and varied, with usually two or three accented, repeated notes which give it a syncopated rhythm" (G. M. Sutton). "The song is endless in its variations, but usually begins with two or three loud, full notes, descending in a more or less confused chipper or trill" (E. H. Eaton).

Calls: "Alarm note a *tchenk*" (E. H. Forbush); "*sst*" (R. Hoffmann); "a sharp metallic *chip*, which is very distinctive when once learned" (E. T. Seton).

Catch phrases: "Maids! maids! maids! hang up your teakettle-ettle-ettle" (H. D. Thoreau); "Hip-hip horray, boys, spring is here!"

Notes: Not only do individual Song Sparrows sing differently at different times, but their songs vary according to localities. Thus the Song Sparrows of Central New York seem to sing with a slightly different cadence than those of the Hudson Valley. Aretus Saunders has recorded over six hundred variations in this bird's song. This would seem to make identifying Song Sparrows by song extremely difficult; and yet that is not the case. Though there is almost infinite variation, each song is enough like the typical so as to be easily placed; and in practice, the Song Sparrow is one of the easier birds to identify by ear.

VESPER SPARROW

Pooecetes gramineus gramineus (Gmelin)

Other names: Eastern Vesper Sparrow, Bay-winged Bunting, Grass Finch, Ground-bird, Bay-winged Sparrow, Road Sparrow.

Record # 1A

Approximate dates when song is abundant: April until July.

Usual location when singing: Usually not far from the ground, though by no means restricted to that area. Often from a low post or fence. It is a bird of the dry pasture, dusty roadsides, and the border of cultivated fields. Most often heard near sundown.

Song: "Somewhat similar to the Song Sparrow but rather louder and clearer" (E. H. Forbush); "two long low notes, succeeded by two higher ones, then descending in chippering trills" (E. H. Eaton); less energetic than the Song Sparrow's song, clearer, sweeter and more plaintive.

Calls: "Alarm note a *chip*, not a *chinck* like the Song Sparrow" (E. H. Forbush).

Notes: Ralph Hoffmann in "Birds of New England," while writing of the song of this bird says, "Beginners have much difficulty in distinguishing the song of this sparrow from that of the Song Sparrow. The opening notes of the latter are very various but almost always three, rather brisk and high. Those of the Vesper Sparrow are two, low, long, and sweet; then after two higher notes the song runs off into a succession of trills, not musical in themselves, but aiding in giving the whole performance more dignity and sweetness than the Song Sparrow's livelier effect."

FIELD SPARROW

Spizella pusilla pusilla (Wilson)

Other names: Eastern Field Sparrow, Bush Sparrow, Huckleberry Bird.

Record # 1A

Approximate dates when song is abundant: April to August.

Usual location when singing: "From a low perch, often the dead branch of a tall bush or small tree in bushy hillside or abandoned field" (T. S. Robert).

Song: "A pensive strain, often varied, usually begins with a few slow, high, clear, prolonged, slurred notes, then accelerates, and finally trails off *diminuendo* in rapid repetitions, fading at its end" (E. H. Forbush). A sweet, simple lay, rarely the same in two birds, but always similar, and always ending in the minor key. "An unusually clear, plaintive whistle" (F. M. Chapman).

Calls: A gentle *"tsip."*

Notes: The Field Sparrow's pensive song is quite distinctive, and easily remembered once it is known. Through the song it is not difficult to recognize this rather nondescript sparrow, for his drab costume and retiring manners make finding him none too easy.

WHITE-THROATED SPARROW

Zonotrichia albicollis (Gmelin)

Other names: Peabody-bird, Canada bird, Canada White-throat.

Record # 1A

Approximate dates when song is abundant: On breeding grounds from arrival in May until mid-July; when migrating in April and May, it is often heard, and also, though less frequently, while passing through in the fall months of October and November.

Usual location when singing: In migration the bird is often heard as it scratches among dead leaves in brush heaps, scrubby, well-watered slashings, bushes and briers. On its nesting grounds in the north woods it is one of the most attractive songsters, and often sings from a perch among the lower branches of a tree or from a bush or sapling.

Song: Numerous variations of the "Poor-Sam-Peabody, Peabody, Peabody" song. It is a rather plaintive lay, often delivered in the minor key.

Calls: A "characteristic, rather metallic call-note" (G. M. Sutton); also "a *sst* similar to the lisp of the Song Sparrow and the Fox Sparrow" (R. Hoffmann).

Catch phrases: "Poor-Sam-Peabody, Peabody, Peabody."
"Sweet Canada, Canada, Canada, Canada."

Notes: The White-throat is one of the most characteristic birds of our northern woods. I recall the first time I identified the song. I had tramped to the top of one of the Adirondacks, and was resting from the exertion in the cool breeze of the summit. From the scrubby blueberry patch just below me I heard this clear, sweet song, as cool and refreshing as the breeze of the mountain top.

WHITE-CROWNED SPARROW

Zonotrichia leucophrys leucophrys (Forster)

Other names: White-browed Crown Sparrow.

Record # 1A

Approximate dates when song is abundant: This bird is only a transient in the eastern United States. It nests in the far north; hence its song rarely is heard except during the time that it is with us in the spring, which, in most localities, is restricted to ten days or two weeks in the middle of May.

Usual location when singing: Around thickets and hedgerows, and not uncommonly around the domicile of man, during its short stay among us. Sings usually from a low perch.

Song: "A soft varied whistle of gentle melancholy" (W. L. Dawson); "a sweet but rather short lay of five to seven notes, first long and clear, and all clear except two next the last which are somewhat blurred, quality of Vesper Sparrow's tone, and diminished toward the end like that of the White-throated Sparrow" (E. H. Forbush).

Calls: "Call note *chink* or *tsip*" (E. H. Forbush), similar to many other sparrows; alarm note a sharp *chip.*

Catch phrases: "More wet wetter wet chee zee" (C. W. Townsend).

Notes: Ernest Thompson Seton says of this handsome sparrow, "Though its season of love and music is spent in the far north, it often favors us with selections of its melodies as it rests in thickets and hedgerows while slowly passing through our country on its northward pilgrimage. Its usual song is like the latter half of the White-throat's familiar refrain, repeated a number of times with a peculiar sad cadence and in a clear, soft whistle that is characteristic of the group." Gambel's Sparrow (*Zonotrichia leucophrys gambeli*) and Nuttall's Sparrow (*Zonotrichia leucophrys nuttalli*) are western subspecies of the White-crowned Sparrows; their songs are similar to those of the eastern bird.

WOOD PEWEE

Myiochanes virens (Linnaeus)

Other names: Eastern Wood Pewee, Pewee, Dead-limb Bird.

Record # 1A

Approximate dates when song is abundant: The second half of May through the summer until well into August. Toward mid-August, though still singing, he abbreviates his song. The Pewee is a constant singer, all day long, right through the heat of the day, and in mid-summer when other birds have ceased, he continues his plaintive song.

Usual location when singing: High up in the trees, in the woods or the woodland border; not uncommon in the elms and maples that shade the village street; or in orchards.

Song: "A plaintive musical *pee-a-wee, pee-wee,* the first half ending with an upward inflection, the latter with a distinct falling" (G. M. Sutton); a simple, pensive song of real sweetness, with a touch of sadness in it. Decidedly in the minor key.

Calls: Around the nest a "*chitter* or *chipper*" (E. H. Forbush); "a low *chit*" (R. Hoffmann).

Catch phrases: "Pee-a-wee."

Notes: The Starling very commonly imitates the song of the Pewee, so that Pewee songs heard in winter or in unlikely places can almost certainly be attributed to the Starling.

PHOEBE

Sayornis phoebe (Latham)

Other names: Eastern Phoebe, Bridge-bird, Phoebe-bird, Bridge Phoebe, House, Barn or Bridge Pewee.

Record # 1A

Approximate dates when song is abundant: Second half of April until July.

Usual location when singing: "Bridge rail, barnyard gate or piazza" (F. M. Chapman); around the habitation of man, from a moderately low perch, such as the barn roof or a telegraph wire. Also frequents the stream bank, where he perches on an overhanging low branch of tree or bush.

Song: "*Fébe*" repeated incessantly, with often a pause of less than two seconds. Has a characteristic habit of flicking its tail sideways after delivering its simple two syllable song that is quite diagnostic. "*preVEE*, as if insisting on that with peculiar emphasis" (H. D. Thoreau).

Calls: "A sharp *chip*" (E. H. Forbush).

Catch phrases: "Phoebe."

Notes: The Phoebe and its relatives, the smaller Flycatchers, are among the most difficult birds to identify by sight. Their voices, however, are distinctive; hence by the aid of our ears, plus a knowledge of their habits and habitats, it is possible to identify these birds in the field, even though their general appearances are very similar.

ALDER FLYCATCHER

Empidonax trailli trailli (Audubon)

Other names: Traill's Flycatcher. (This name is now given to the western race of the species.)

Record # 1A

Approximate dates when song is abundant: Mid-May to mid-July.

Usual location when singing: "Either an exposed perch, where he may be seen jerking his head violently, or concealed in the leafy twigs" (R. Hoffmann). Not over ten to twenty feet from the ground, in well-watered slashings and clearings, among alders and willows.

Song: Phoebe-o: or a "short staccato *'We're-here'* or *'Ezee-e-up'* with accent on the last syllables in each case" (W. Brewster).

Calls: "A sharp *Pip*" (R. Hoffmann).

Catch phrases: "We're-here."

Notes: To my ear the song of the Alder Flycatcher suggests that of the Phoebe, but it is three syllables instead of two and differently accented. In fact, my introduction to the Alder Flycatcher was when I first recorded his voice, some years ago, and found out later that what I thought was a Phoebe with an unusual song was his relative, the Alder Flycatcher.

WHIP-POOR-WILL

Antrostomus vociferus vociferus (Wilson)

Other names: Eastern Whip-poor-will.

Record # 1A

Approximate dates when song is abundant: Early to mid-May to about July 10th, in the early evening for a couple of hours beginning about one-half hour after sunset, and again before dawn.

Usual location when singing: Bushy fields or scrubby hillside, where he finds a low bush from which to deliver his odd song; occasionally from an old barrel or shed roof or even a farm door stone or mounting block.

Song: Whip'-poor-will', repeated ad infinitum; sometimes if one is very close one hears a decided *chuck* before the *whip*, but this is not always the case. The timing of the song varies considerably, some birds being slow and deliberate in their rendition; while others suggest being excited and in a hurry.

Calls: Numerous odd sounds including "a peculiar *aw-aw-aw-aw*" (O. W. Knight); "a low grunting like *däck däck* and another like *zue see, zue see*" (C. Bendire); "female calls her young with a gentle *coo*" (E. H. Forbush).

Catch phrases: "Whip-poor-will."

Notes: The Whip-poor-will is noted for his persistence. One observer has counted 700 refrains of his repetitious song before he stopped. I have heard the bird sing steadily for over ten minutes, with hardly enough pause between repetitions to enable him to catch his breath.

VEERY

Hylocichla fuscescens fuscescens (Stephens)

Other names: Wilson's Thrush, Cathedral-bird.

Record # 1B

Approximate dates when song is abundant: The second half of May until mid-July.

Usual location when singing: From the dense thicket of low moist woodlands, wooded swamp, *etc.* Most often heard at dusk.

Song: "A weird ringing monotone of blended alto and soprano notes. Neither notes nor letters can tell one of its peculiar quality" (F. M. Chapman).

Calls: "A penetrating *zeu*" (G. M. Sutton); "a sharply whistled *pheeu*" (E. H. Eaton); "a clearly whistled *whèe-o* or *whèe-you*, the first note higher, and a somewhat softer *too-whee* or *teweù*, with the first note lower" (F. M. Chapman).

Catch phrases: "I'm so sl-e-e-e-e-e-p-e-e-."

Doctor Chapman suggests that it may be recalled by "the syllables *vee-r-r-hu* repeated eight or nine times around a series of intertwining circles."

Notes: The Veery's song always brings to my mind the picture of our beautiful northern lakes. It is around their wooded shores that the ringing, hymnlike song is often heard. The western sub-species, the Willow Thrush (*Hylocichla fuscescens salicicola*), has a song that is indistinguishable from the eastern bird's.

OLIVE-BACKED THRUSH

Hylocichla ustulata swainsoni (Tschudi)

Other names: Swainson's Thrush, Swamp Robin.

Record # 1B

Approximate dates when song is abundant: June to mid-July.

Usual location when singing: From a perch high up in a tree; a bird of our northern woods. On the breeding grounds more often heard than seen.

Song: "The first note loudest and most liquid, after which the melody becomes rapidly fainter, seeming to dissolve upon the ear like the spent vibrations of a stringed instrument" (E. Bicknell). "It begins with two or three notes almost exactly like a Veery's song, then changes to a refrain like that of the Hermit or Wood Thrush, and ends with a distinct rising inflection" (T. S. Roberts).

Calls: "A *queep*, a whistling *whit*, a *chuck* of alarm, a feeble *tsip* and a cry *chick*, *chick-a sit*. Alarm note on breeding grounds *che-urr, che-urr*" (E. H. Forbush).

Notes: Hoffmann, in "Birds of New England," says, "It is unmistakably the voice of a thrush, like a Veery's song inverted, going up instead of down the scale." It is as an inverted Veery's song that the beginner will find it easiest to recognize this charming thrush's song.

63

WOOD THRUSH

Hylocichla mustelina (Gmelin)

Record # 1B

Approximate dates when song is abundant: Mid-May until late July and sometimes as late as the middle of August.

Usual location when singing: The edge of the woods or well-shaded lawn where there are many big trees. Sings from a perch on a limb, not infrequently from the upper half of the tree.

Song: "A pure, clear, sweet, expressive, liquid refrain, often with a bell-like ending; usually composed of a series of triplets, each beginning with a high note, then a low one, then a trill, often highest of all, but the different phrases varying in pitch. It is calm, unhurried, peaceful, and unequaled both in power and beauty by any other woodland songster of New England. That of the Hermit Thrush is perhaps finer, though not so loud" (E. H. Forbush in "Birds of Massachusetts").

Calls: "A liquid *quirt,* a low *tut tut,* a sharp *pit pit* or *pip pip* and a shrill *tsee tsee*" (E. H. Forbush).

Notes: Doctor Chapman says of this almost indescribably beautiful song, that it is "calm and restful, ringing through the woods like a hymn of praise, pure and clear from a thankful heart; the flute-like opening notes are an invitation to its haunts, a call from nature to yield ourselves to the ennobling influences of the forest."

"OH, LISTEN TO THE MOCKINGBIRD."

The dynamic microphone is set up on a post 250 feet from the
truck in an attempt to capture the mockingbird's song.

HERMIT THRUSH

Hylocichla guttata faxoni Bangs and Penard

Other names: Eastern Hermit Thrush, Swamp Angel, Swamp Robin.

Record # 1B

Approximate dates when song is abundant: Mid-May till late July; occasionally the song will be heard after that date, and even well into August. I have heard the bird sing a few snatches of its song, once or twice, during the spring migration.

Usual location when singing: In the thick of the northern woods. If we are adventurous we may have the pleasure of watching a Hermit Thrush sing; but we must be willing to go into the very thick of the forest. Here, from the top of a bare stub or from the lower branch of a small tree, we shall find the songster giving voice to his inspiring lay.

Song: "Several strains of different pitch, each introduced by a clear, flute-like note, sometimes slightly *crescendo*, then followed by two or three (sometimes four) higher, vibratory notes; of soprano or mezzo-soprano quality, ascending and descending in tone, in no fixed order" (E. H. Forbush).

Calls: "A low chuck" (F. M. Chapman); "a harsh *speke* note" (E. H. Forbush); somewhat similar to the Catbird's mew, and usually heard only on the breeding grounds; "a low *tway*, suggesting the call of the Towhee" (H. R. Carey).

Notes: Language is all too restricted to attempt adequately to describe the song of this thrush, our most superb songster. Perhaps John Burroughs has done it as well as any one, for he does not attempt to describe the song, but tells of the emotions that it inspires. "Mounting toward the upland again, I pause reverently as the hush and stillness of twilight comes upon the woods. It is the sweetest, ripest hour of the day. And as the Hermit's evening hymn goes up from the deep solitude below me, I experience that serene exaltation of sentiment of which music, literature and religion are but faint types and symbols."

BOBOLINK

Dolichonyx oryzivorus (Linnaeus)

Other names: Reed-bird, Rice-bird, Skunk Blackbird.

Record # 1B

Approximate dates when song is abundant: First or second week in May to the first week in July, or mid-July at the latest.

Usual location when singing: Grass or clover fields and meadows are the haunts of the Bobolink; "from the tops of neighboring trees, or from some bending weed or tuft of grass. Often they sing in the air, either gliding with curved wings or chasing each other furiously over the fields" (R. Hoffmann).

Song: "An indescribable bubbling medley from which the bird received its name, often ending in *chee* or *speee*" (E. H. Forbush); almost invariably a characteristic *clink* suggesting broken china being struck, appears somewhere in the song.

Calls: "A metallic *chinck*" (F. M. Chapman); "call notes sounding like *träck, träck,* or *tchâe, tchâe* or *killink, killink*" (Bendire); "*chah,* a harsh alarm note similar to that of the blackbird" (F. G. Ashbrook).

Notes: "The Bobolink's song is a marvel of bird music. It seems to spring from an inexhaustible supply of strange syllables and genuine musical notes, offered in a tumultuous jumble as profligate as the manner in which the bird lets himself fall into the grass while continuing to sing" (G. M. Sutton). The Bobolink is very regular in his appearance in the spring, often, in certain places, first being recorded on the same day each year. Unlike many other species, he is in full song on the day he arrives.

WINTER WREN

Nannus hiemalis hiemalis (Vieillot)

Other names: Eastern Winter Wren.

Record # 1B

Approximate dates when song is abundant: May and June.

Usual location when singing: In the forest, sometimes from a tree top; but more often from a dead stub or log while close to the ground, or while hopping about in the thicket.

Song: "A rippling, flowing melody" (F. G. Ashbrook); "tinkling, rippling, full of trills and grace notes" (E. Bicknell); "surprisingly loud for so small a bird; it is long, the first part ending in a trill, and the second part often ending in a trill at least an octave higher than the first; but there are many variations" (E. H. Forbush).

Calls: A sharp *tick* repeated several times in quick succession, numerous *chimps*, *chirrs*, *etc.*, given either singly or repeated a number of times.

Notes: John Burroughs has written about the Winter Wren's song. "It has all the vivacity and versatility of the canary, without any of its shrillness. Its song is indeed a little cascade of melody." Each individual has his own preference as to which of the woodland voices is the most beautiful. My choice is the Winter Wren. For pure beauty and joyfulness, to me, this is our finest sylvan sound.

CAROLINA WREN

Thryothorus ludovicianus ludovicianus (Latham)

Other names: Great Carolina Wren, Mocking-Wren, Teakettle Bird.

Record # 1B

Approximate dates when song is abundant: March to July. (The Carolina Wren is one of the few birds whose song can be heard in any month of the year.)

Usual location when singing: In the brush, tangle or thicket.

Song: "A loud and clear whistle; can be heard a quarter of a mile; very variable" (E. H. Forbush); "common forms *twip pity; twip pity; whiddy you, whiddy you, whiddy you, thri-ou, thri-ou, thri-ou*" (R. Hoffmann); commoner notes resemble "*whee-udel, whee-udel, whee-udel* and *tea-kettle, tea-kettle, tea-kettle*" (F. M. Chapman).

Calls: "Innumerable *clacks*, metallic rattles, musical trills and *k-r-ings*" (E. H. Eaton); "alarm note a rather smooth *peurr*" (E. H. Forbush).

Catch phrases: "Sweetheart, sweetheart, sweetheart."
"Tea-kettle, tea-kettle, tea-kettle."

Notes: Certain notes of the Carolina Wren resemble those of the Cardinal and the Tufted Titmouse. As these birds are often found together—they are all birds that are common in the south, and rare north of New York City—it is well for a beginner to identify the singer by eye as well as by ear, until he is well acquainted with the songs.

HOUSE WREN

Troglodytes aëdon aëdon Vieillot

Other names: Eastern House Wren, Jenny Wren, Wood Wren.

Record # 1B

Approximate dates when song is abundant: May until the end of July or early August.

Usual location when singing: In the garden or apple orchard, about man's habitations.

Song: "A characteristic, bubbling, gurgling warble" (E. H. Eaton); "a gushing, forcible, rather shrill ditty" (T. S. Roberts); "a rather loud, hurried, bubbling outpouring, shrill, ecstatic and indescribable" (E. H. Forbush).

Calls: "Scolding-note a harsh grating chatter, often uttered by the bird from its hiding-place in a stone wall or a brush heap" (R. Hoffmann).

Notes: Any one who has spent any time in the country must know the House Wren. He is such a personality. His song, appearance and manners are so individual. When singing he often holds his tail pointed downward; at other times, especially when scolding, his tail is cocked over his back.

LONG-BILLED MARSH WREN

Telmatodytes palustris palustris (Wilson)

Other names: Marsh Wren, Cat-tail Wren.

Record # 1B

Approximate dates when song is abundant: The latter half of May till late July.

Usual location when singing: In the cattail marshes, and tall reedy grasses bordering rivers or ponds, sometimes in salt marshes.

Song: "A bubbling, rippling, but somewhat monotonous series of notes" (E. H. Forbush); "a mixture of clicking, lisping, purring and sweet sputtering about them all which is not at all unpleasant to the ear" (W. L. Dawson).

Calls: "An energetic *tschuk*" (R. Hoffmann); also an alarmed chattering.

Notes: Dr. C. W. Townsend writes: "The song begins with a scrape like the tuning of a violin followed by a trill which bubbles, gurgles, or rattles, depending no doubt on the skill or mood of the performer; at times liquid and musical; at other times rattling and harsh, but always vigorous. It ends abruptly but is generally followed by a short musical whistle or a trill, as if the wren were drawing in breath after its efforts. I have heard one sing fifteen times in a minute. The bird reminds me of a musical toy wound up to go off at frequent intervals."

NORTHERN WATER-THRUSH

Seiurus noveboracensis noveboracensis (Gmelin)

Other names: Water-thrush, Water-wagtail.

Record # 2A

Approximate dates when song is abundant: May until early July.

Usual location when singing: In damp forest or wooded swamp, most likely to be found in the brush and among the fallen logs; when singing this Water-thrush often selects a perch well up in a tree, not infrequently the very topmost branch.

Song: "*Shing-ching-ching, chee-chee-chee che-che-ch-ch*" (J. B. May); "*Quit-quit-quit-que-quewe-u*" (F. G. Ashbrook); "a ringing, bubbling warble, swift and emphatic, made up of two parts, barely divided, the second lower-toned and *diminuendo*" (G. Thayer); "also a quicker and longer flight song" (E. H. Forbush).

Calls: "Sharp steely alarm note, *clink*" (F. M. Chapman).

Catch phrases: "Hurry, hurry, hurry, pretty, pretty, pretty" (G. M. Sutton).

Notes: The Northern Water-thrush's melodious song, as it breaks the silence of the woodland swamp, is so loud as to be almost startling. The closely related Louisiana Water-thrush, whose range is more southerly, also has a song of rare beauty, though it is so different from the northern species that confusion is unlikely. The western sub-species of the Northern Water-thrush, Grinnell's Water-thrush, *Seiurus noveboracensis notabilis*, has a song that is, to all practical purposes, the same as the Northern Water-thrush's, or at least authorities are unable to separate them.

RED-SHOULDERED HAWK

Buteo lineatus lineatus (Gmelin)

Other names: Northern Red-shouldered Hawk, Chicken Hawk, Hen Hawk, Winter Hawk.

Record # 2A

Approximate dates when song (scream) is abundant: Late March to early July.

Usual location where heard: Well-watered woodlands, not far from open fields and swamps. "It may be seen circling high overhead, or a pair may be seen over low, swampy woods, screaming, and soaring higher and higher" (R. Hoffmann).

Song or call: A "screaming cry of *Keè-you keè-you*" (F. M. Chapman); "a rather prolonged *tee-ur tee-ur*, the last syllable drawn out, with a falling inflection at the end" (E. H. Forbush).

Notes: The Blue Jay at times imitates the scream of the Red-shouldered so that positive identification by sound alone is risky. However, the bird can often be identified by its sound when it is soaring so high that the observer cannot make out field marks, and could, without recognition of its voice, identify it only as a hawk. The Broad-winged Hawk has a much lighter scream, though somewhat similar to that of the Red-shouldered Hawk, but it is so much feebler that it should not be confusing. Also the birds rarely nest in the same parts of the country. Thus in the Adirondacks we find the Broad-winged nesting, while elsewhere in New York State the Red-shouldered Hawk is likely to be the breeding bird.

LOUISIANA WATER-THRUSH

Seiurus motacilla (Vieillot)

Other names: Large-billed Water-thrush, Southern Water-thrush, Water Wagtail.

Record # 2A

Approximate dates when song is abundant: This is one of the earliest of our song birds to be heard in full song, and also one of the first to cease singing. Thus around the bubbling rushing brook where he makes his home, one is likely to hear the Louisiana Water-thrush as early as April 10th, and the song becomes rare after May 25th.

Usual location when singing: The bird usually makes its home in a rocky glen in deeply shaded woods, where a rushing brook tumbles and splashes over a stony bed. In that type of habitat you will find this songster, more often hearing than seeing him. He frequently sings from a high perch, often from the center of some tall tree, and finding him is a trick in itself, though his loud, wild song is sure proof of his presence.

Song: Reminiscent of the Northern Water-thrush, "being quite as loud, almost as rapid, and commencing in nearly the same way but lacking the beautiful *crescendo* termination, and altogether, a less fine performance. A short song, *pseur, pseur per see ser*" (William Brewster). Opinions differ; while Mr. Brewster prefers the Northern Water-thrush, a number of competent ornithologists think the Louisiana's song is the finer. Though there is little chance of mistaking one for the other after one is familiar with them, they are both clear wild carols, of surprising musical quality.

Call notes: A loud, ringing *chip.*

Notes: "As a songster the Water-thrush is without a rival. His song is not to be compared with the clear-voiced carol of the Rose-breasted Grosbeak, the plaintive chant of the Field Sparrow, or the hymnlike melody of the true thrushes; it is of a different kind. It is the untamable spirit of the bird rendered in music. There is an almost fierce wildness in its ringing notes. On rare occasions he is inspired to voice his passion in a flight-song, which so far exceeds his usual performance that even the memory of it is thrilling" (Frank M. Chapman).

BALD EAGLE

Haliaeetus leucocephalus leucocephalus (Linnaeus)

Other names: Southern Bald Eagle, American Eagle, Bald-headed Eagle, White-headed Eagle, Gray Eagle (young).

Record # 2A

Approximate dates when scream is most often heard: Late winter to early summer.
Usual location where seen or heard: In forested regions near sea, river or large bodies of water.

Voice: "A high-pitched, cackling scream" (E. H. Forbush); "a barking squeal, sometimes very high and thin" (G. M. Sutton); "the cry of the male is a loud clear *cac-cac-cac*, quite different from that of the female; the call of the latter is more harsh and often broken" (W. L. Ralph).

Notes: The Eagle's scream of which we have heard so much actually is a most disappointing sound. For so majestic a bird to possess so thin a squeal comes as rather a shock. Many of our small song birds, the Northern Water-thrush or the Ruby-crowned Kinglet, for example, not only make more beautiful sounds—that might be expected—but their voices are considerably louder and wilder.

ROBIN

Turdus migratorius migratorius Linnaeus

Other names: Eastern Robin, American Robin, Robin Redbreast.

Record # 2A

Approximate dates when song is abundant: Late March or early April until the end of July.

Usual location when singing: Almost anywhere, from a tree, high or low, or a telegraph wire, or pole; on the roof of barn, shed or house, usually, however, not too near the ground.

Song: "A series of phrases rising and falling, four often constituting a series, which is then repeated or varied" (R. Hoffmann).

Calls: "Alarm note a *chirp* varied in pitch and volume, a shrill squeal or scream when in great fear" (E. H. Forbush); a variety of calls including "a rapid, rather explosive *puck-puck-puck-puck-puck; skeek skeek*" (E. H. Forbush); and "a clear *tee-urp*" (G. F. Simmons); "a shrill *tsee tsee*, often followed by a low *tut tut*" (R. Hoffmann).

Catch phrases: "Kill 'im, cure 'im, give 'im physic." "Cheerily cheer-up cheerily cheer-up," or "cheer-up cheer cheer cheer-up."

Notes: The Robin's song is perhaps the best known of American birds'. His is a long day. He is often the first to greet the sun, starting his singing when light is still hardly visible in the eastern sky, and at night, well after dark, and long after the other birds have stopped, his evening song adds charm to the twilight.

ROSE-BREASTED GROSBEAK

Hedymeles ludovicianus (Linnaeus)

Other names: Throat-cut, Potato-bug Bird.

Record # 2A

Approximate dates when song is abundant: Before mid-May until late July or early August.

Usual location when singing: From tall trees. Often sings in flight, and is known to sing while on the nest while relieving the female during incubation.

Song: "A beautiful, sweet, mellow warble, resembling slightly the Robin's song, but smoother, softer, sweeter, more mellifluous" (E. H. Forbush); that of "a glorified Robin" (J. Burroughs); "a fine, powerful warble, with some of the cadence of the Robin's song though faster" (R. Hoffmann); " a rich, full, whistling carol nearly always beginning with a sharp *chip*" (F. G. Ashbrook).

Calls: "*eek*" (G. M. Sutton); "alarm note a sharp, metallic *chick*" (R. Hoffmann); "a deep-toned *chip*" (F. G. Ashbrook); a loud, sharp, questioning "*peek peek*" (E. H. Eaton).

Notes: To the beginner the songs of the Rose-breasted Grosbeak and the Robin are quite confusing. The usual note at the beginning of each warble described by Ashbrook (see above) as a sharp *chip*, is a very good clue. If then the song has the sweet, smooth quality, you can feel fairly sure that you are hearing the Rose-breasted Grosbeak, and not the Robin.

SCARLET TANAGER

Piranga erythromelas Vieillot

Other names: Fire Bird, Black-winged Red Bird.

Record # 2A

Approximate dates when song is abundant: About May 7th to mid-July.

Usual location when singing: In the tree-tops of open woodlands.

Song: "A slightly hoarse carol of similar tempo to that of the Robin" (E. H. Forbush); though slightly faster; and yet it seems to have a lazy quality which is probably due to the furriness or hoarseness of the song. "Rhythmical, hoarse, and not long sustained, suggests a Robin with a cold" (R. Hoffmann); "much like a Robin's but it is more alto, and is harsher" (G. M. Sutton).

Calls: "*Chip-chirr*" (F. M. Bailey); "*chi-perr*" (G. M. Sutton); "a sharp *chip* or *chip-churr*" (F. G. Ashbrook).

Notes: One would suppose that because of his gaudy plumage the Scarlet Tanager would be more often seen than heard. This is not the case; the bird keeps well up in the trees, and strangely enough, is able to lose himself from sight in the green foliage. If one learns his song, however, one will find him much more common than sight records alone would indicate.

BALTIMORE ORIOLE

Icterus galbula (Linnaeus)

Other names: Golden Robin, Hang-bird, Hang-nest, Fire-Hang-bird, Oriole, Fire-bird.

Record # 2A

Approximate dates when song is abundant: About May 10th to late June or early July.

Usual location when singing: From the upper half of a tree; has a distinct preference for nesting in elms.

Song: "A clear, varied whistle" (F. G. Ashbrook); "a succession of clear, wild, rounded notes easily imitated by whistling, but difficult to describe; many variations" (E. H. Forbush); there is also much individual variation.

Calls: Alarm note: "a long rattling chatter" (E. H. Forbush); "a plaintive whistle" (F. G. Ashbrook); "the female during the mating season whistles two or three notes similar to the male's" (R. Hoffmann); the young birds are quite noisy, their food call which is most persistent, being quoted by F. M. Chapman as *dee dee dee dee.*

Notes: The Baltimore Oriole's song is a very good example of how bird song varies among individuals of the same species. The song is not particularly difficult to identify, and yet two birds rarely sing exactly alike; and as the season progresses an individual will improve and embroider his song.

CARDINAL

Richmondena cardinalis cardinalis (Linnaeus)

Other names: Eastern Cardinal, Redbird, Virginia Cardinal or Redbird, Cardinal Grosbeak, Kentucky Cardinal.

Record # 2A

Approximate dates when song is abundant: March to July, heard occasionally where it is resident almost any month in the year.

Usual location when singing: On cultivated lands and about dwellings. They usually perch not too far from the ground.

Song: "A loud, clear whistle, into which usually enters quite frequently the sound of *q!q!q!* and a peculiar long-drawn-out *e-è*" (O. T. Miller); "*whoit, whoit, whoit, etc., ku-ku-ku, etc.*" (R. Hoffmann); female also whistles musically.

Calls: "A sharp abrupt *tsip*" (O. T. Miller); "A metallic chirp" (G. M. Sutton).

Catch phrase: "What cheer, what cheer."

Notes: The female as well as the male of this species indulges in song. This is quite unusual. Her song, however, is somewhat softer, though by no means inferior to the male's. There is no appreciable difference in the songs of the various sub-species, the Florida and Louisiana Cardinal, and the more northerly representative of the species.

CATBIRD

Dumetella carolinensis (Linnaeus)

Record # 2B

Approximate dates when song is abundant: May until mid-July. The song is occasionally heard in October, though then it is extremely soft, and one would suspect that the bird was a great distance off. The scolding catlike mew is heard all summer long, in fact, until October, when the bird turns southward for the winter.

Usual location when singing: The Catbird is a bird of the thicket and dense shrubbery, and shows a preference for the syringa and lilac bushes of our gardens. He usually sings while perched in or near his favorite haunt. He also frequents the thickets near streams, and is rarely found far from water.

Song: A succession of phrases, each one delivered as a positive statement complete in itself, "similar to that of the Brown Thrasher and Mockingbird, but softer, often sweeter, though frequently marred by harsh phrases, and in some cases occasionally interlarded with imitations of other species" (E. H. Forbush); The Catbird often ruins—(as far as humans are concerned)—his otherwise lovely song by interjections of his call, which, as his name implies, suggests a cat's mew. The songs are extremely varied, some birds' songs far surpassing in beauty those of other members of the species.

Calls: Most commonly "a complaining snarling *mew* resembling that of a cat, also a soft mellow chuck" (E. H. Forbush); "a grating chatter *kak kak kak*" (R. Hoffmann); "*trat-tat-tat-tat* uttered very quickly" (E. A. Samuels); "some notes resembling slightly the call of the Blue Jay" (E. H. Forbush).

Notes: The Catbird is a consummate mimic, the Mockingbird alone surpassing him among American birds in this art. Not only will he mimic bird kind but he also imitates frogs, mammals, and mechanical sounds from nature. These mimicries he incorporates in his song. He is a busybody among birds; and like his namesake the cat is endowed with infinite curiosity. He often scolds as he goes about his business of looking into other folks' affairs.

A Meadow Lark on His Singing Perch.

From a motion picture taken by Arthur
A. Allen.

The Horned Owl.

From a moving picture taken by Arthur A. Allen.

BROWN THRASHER

Toxostoma rufum (Linnaeus)

Other names: Brown Thrush, Red Mavis, Planting Bird.

Record # 2B

Approximate dates when song is abundant: Late April or early May to the first week of July.

Usual location when singing: "The male sings from a high perch, often the uppermost spray of a tall tree, with tail depressed" (R. Hoffmann); though ordinarily a rather shy, retiring bird, when singing he seeks an exposed position; "during the building of the nest, which requires six to ten days, and in which both birds take part, the song of the male is heard more from cover" (E. H. Forbush).

Song: "A succession of phrases of two to four syllables, loud, clear, rich, musical and of great variety, each one delivered as a positive statement complete in itself, and unrelated to the rest, with a brief pause after it—all bearing considerable resemblance to the songs of the Mockingbird or Catbird, but mostly original with occasionally an imitation of some other bird's notes" (E. H. Forbush).

Calls: "A loud *smack*, a plaintive whistle *ti-you-oo* or *wheurrr*, and a sharp *click*, also a hissing or wheezing sound" (E. H. Forbush).

Catch phrases: "Drop it, drop it, cover it up, cover it up—pull it up, pull it up, pull it up, pull it up" (H. D. Thoreau).

Notes: The Brown Thrasher is one of the finest singers in our region; some authorities even give him preference over the Mockingbird. Thus Arthur T. Wayne says: "To my ear the song of the Brown Thrasher is sweeter, richer and wilder than the Mockingbird, and as a musician he is simply incomparable."

On the record there are a few notes which a person well versed in bird song can recognize as the Towhee. This bird was in the background when the recording was made.

MOCKINGBIRD

Mimus polyglottos polyglottos (Linnaeus)

Other names: Eastern Mockingbird, Mocker, Mock-bird.

Record # 2B

Approximate dates when song is abundant: Early February till August; in the southern United States his song will occasionally be heard at almost any time of year.

Usual location when singing: Anywhere in the open, rarely in the woods, though sometimes in the wood border. From the top of a tall tree, in flight, on the roof of house or shed, on a telegraph wire or pole, or in a low bush. His tastes are most catholic. "Watch the Mockingbird some spring morning, as with ruffled feathers and drooping wings he sits on the topmost bough of a neighboring tree and pours out the beautiful story of his love. At times the very intensity of the music within his breast seems to lift him many feet in the air. With dangling legs and carelessly flapping wings, he drops again to his perch, singing the while, anon he descends to the earth for a moment, a few rapid hops in the grass, and he bounds again into the air with scarcely an intermission in his song" (T. G. Pearson).

Song: "A sweet thrasher-like medley, interspersed with many imitations of notes, calls, and songs of other birds; also a rapturous, indescribable flight-song by day or night, much given on moonlit nights" (E. H. Forbush). The Mockingbird's song beggars description; for variety, and originality, no American bird song can compare with it. It always affects me with wonder and amazement; and gives me the thrill of joy which a child would experience when listening to a perfect, and most artistic buffoon.

Calls: "A harsh *chuck*" (A. H. Howell); "a loud *smack* and a harsh, grating *chair*" (R. Hoffmann); "a *chuck* or *chick* and a scolding note (almost Veery-like) *whee-e-e*" (J. A. Farley).

Notes: The Mockingbird is our most noted American songster, and well deserves his popularity. He not only sings for most of the year, where he is resident, but is not ashamed of his song. He lets us hear it, both night and day; and as he is a bird of our gardens and parks, rather than of the less populated woods, he is constantly with us. He is especially partial to fine, moonlit nights, indulging in some of his finest singing on these occasions. He is our greatest imitator, though not every member of the race is given to mimicry, many having only their racial notes.

YELLOW-BREASTED CHAT

Icteria virens virens (Linnaeus)

Record # 2B

Approximate dates when song is abundant: Mid-May to mid-July or a little later.

Usual location when singing: A tree, rarely over forty feet high, in bushy pastures, briar-patches or deserted orchards. The calls which are practically indistinguishable from the song except in the timing and the manner of deliverance, are usually heard from the thicket or brush cover.

Song: "Impossible of adequate description; songs and calls are all mixed up; an exceedingly eccentric and varied medley of *quits, caws, toots, whistles, mews, etc.*; and in the breeding season some really good music on occasion" (E. H. Forbush).

Calls: "*Chŭt chŭt*" (F. M. Chapman); "a loud *tŏo tŏo tŏo*, a whistled *whit* and various clucking and mewing sounds" (R. Hoffmann); a crow-like *caw*, which like the other calls is often used while singing.

Notes: The Chat is not difficult to identify when singing. No other bird is quite so eccentric and clownish. "Such a medley of whistling, chuckling, barking and mewing sounds proceeds from no other bird, unless it be the Mockingbird" (E. H. Forbush); and the Mockingbird always adds sweeter and purer sounds, while the Chat is an out-and-out buffoon. He is reputed also, to be an accomplished ventriloquist.

YELLOW WARBLER

Dendroica aestiva aestiva (Gmelin)

Other names: Eastern Yellow Warbler, Summer Yellow-bird, Wild Canary, Yellow-bird, Blue-eyed Warbler, Summer Warbler.

Record # 2B

Approximate dates when song is abundant: Through May, June and July.

Usual location when singing: Gardens, shrubbery and lawns, rather than the woods; singing from a tree perch, usually not from the top of the taller trees, often from sapling or bush; also sings while moving around in the bushes.

Song: "*Wee-chee, chee, chee, cher-wee*" (F. M. Chapman); "*che-wee, che-wee, che-wee, che-wee*" (F. G. Ashbrook); and numerous variations.

Calls: A rather loud *chip*; a decisive *dzt*.

Catch phrases: "Sweet sweet sweet, sweeter, sweetest" (A. A. Allen); "sweet sweet sweet sweetie" (E. H. Eaton).

Notes: The song of the Yellow Warbler is one of our commonest. It is often difficult to distinguish it from that of the Redstart and Chestnut-sided. Still there is a difference in quality. It is loud and penetrating, and there is a smoothness that makes it individual. The Yellow Warbler's song, though simple, has a pleasing, unaffected sound that is quite as fascinating as the more complicated warbler songs. On the record several variations of the common songs are given.

CHESTNUT-SIDED WARBLER

Dendroica pensylvanica (Linnaeus)

Record # 2B

Approximate dates when song is abundant: First to third week in May through July.

Usual location when singing: Scrubby clearings and the bushy, woodland border; "in low roadside and brookside thickets, or in sproutlands rather recently cut over" (E. H. Forbush); from a tree or bush, often the topmost branch.

Song: Two main songs, the most common given as *te te te te we che*, or *twit-a wit-a wit-a-wit-wee-chee*! Another given as *wée-see-wée-see-wée-see*; endless variations of these are also heard, many of them so like other warblers as to be quite confusing.

Calls: "A soft *tsip*, a rather loud *chip*" (E. H. Forbush).

Catch phrases: "Sweet, sweet, sweet, I'll switch you" (A. A. Allen); "Very very pleased to meetcha" (R. Hoffmann).

Notes: "Songs with no fixed form we guess to be the Chestnut-sided, because it sounds like its voice, and when we locate the bird we are right. Yet to describe that quality of voice and to say just how it differs from the Yellow Warbler, Magnolia Warbler or Redstart seems impossible" (A. A. Saunders).

MARYLAND YELLOW-THROAT

Geothlypis trichas brachidactyla (Swainson)

Other names: Northern Yellow-throat, Black-masked Warbler, Ground Warbler, Yellow-throat.

Record # 2B

Approximate dates when song is abundant: May to late July.

Usual location when singing: A swamp inhabitant, but also in wet places along roadsides and wall, the edge of moist woods and the brookside. Song delivered from a low perch; rarely stays long in one place, but hopping from bush to bush as it works and sings. Rarely over ten feet from the ground.

Song: Wichity wichity wichity, or " *rapity, rapity, rapity*" (F. M. Chapman), express it about as well as written characters can; there are, however, many variations. Hoffmann, in "Birds of New England," calls attention to three forms of the song. "It varies in different localities, but the same form is generally used by birds of one region; there are dialects, in other words."

Calls: "Quickly repeated *chack*, varying to *chit, pit, quit*" (F. M. Chapman); "a harsh, rather loud *tschack*" (G. M. Sutton); "a rapid wren-like chatter" (R. Hoffmann).

Catch phrases: "I beseech you, I beseech you, I beseech you, I beseech you" (F. M. Chapman).

Notes: South of Pennsylvania the common Maryland Yellow-throat is a different sub-species, *Geothlypis trichas trichas*, but there is no appreciable difference in its song. Farther south, however, a third sub-species exists, the Florida Yellow-throat, *Geothlypis trichas ignota*, and its song differs recognizably from that of the northern birds.

GREAT HORNED OWL

Bubo virginianus virginianus (Gmelin)

Other names: Cat Owl, Hoot Owl, Big Owl.

Record # 2B

Approximate dates when hoot is likely to be heard: February, or even earlier, till mid-June. Sometimes the hoot is regularly heard again in the fall; and occasionally at any time of the year.

Usual location when hooting: In well-watered forests; a bird of the woods. Heard at night, most active at dusk and on moonlit nights.

Hoot and calls: A deep-toned hoot; variations of hooting syllables, most commonly *hoo, hoo-hoo, hoo hoo*; or *whoo, hoo-hoo-hoo, whoo whoo*; "more rarely a powerful, bloodcurdling shriek; a loud *waugh hoo*, first syllable accented, and with rising inflection, also many short jabbering or laughing tones" (E. H. Forbush).

Notes: The hoot is often mistaken for the distant baying of a deep-voiced dog, which sound it closely resembles. The bloodcurdling scream "is often wrongly attributed to a wild cat. The probability is that a wild cat in its wildest fit of anger or alarm could not produce a sound half so loud and terrifying" (G. M. Sutton).

BIBLIOGRAPHY OF THE SUBJECT

THE following are some of the chief publications which contain information on bird song. The authors are mentioned alphabetically.

ALLEN, A. A.: 1920. "Learning Bird Song," *Bird Lore*, vol. 22.

ALLEN, A. A.: 1930. "The Book of Bird Life," D. Van Nostrand, N. Y.

ALLEN, F. H.: 1919. "The Evolution of Bird Song," *Auk*, vol. 36.

ASHBROOK, FRANK G.: 1931. "Birds of America." Whitman Publishing Co., Racine, Wis.

CHAPMAN, FRANK M.: 1932. "Handbook of Birds of Eastern North America," Appleton, N. Y.

CHAPMAN, FRANK M.: 1907. "The Warblers of North America," Appleton, N. Y.

CHENEY, S. P.: 1892. "Wood Notes Wild, Notations of Bird Song," Boston.

COFFIN, LUCY V. B.: 1928. "Individuality in Bird Song," Wilson Bulletin, vol. 40.

EATON, ELON H.: 1910. "Birds of New York," N. Y. State Museum, Albany.

FORBUSH, EDWARD H.: 1929. "Birds of Massachusetts," Norwood Press, Norwood, Mass.

FUERTES, LOUIS A.: 1913-14. "Impressions of the Voices of Tropical Birds," *Bird Lore*, vols. 15, 16.

GRISCOM, LUDLOW: 1923. "Birds of the N. Y. City Region." Amer. Mus. of Nat'l Hist., N. Y.

HAWKINS, C. J.: 1918 and 1922. "Sexual Selection and Bird Song." *Auk*, vols. 35, 39.

HOFFMANN, RALPH: 1904. "A Guide to Birds of New England," Houghton Mifflin, N. Y.

MATTHEWS, F. SCHUYLER: 1904. "Field Book of Wild Birds and Their Music," G. P. Putnam's Sons, N. Y.

MORRIS, STANLEY: 1925. "Bird Song," H. F. & G. Witherby, London.

MOUSLEY, H.: 1919. "The Singing Tree," *Auk*, vol. 36.

NICHOLS, J. T.: 1920. "Limicoline Voices," *Auk*, vol. 37.

ROBERTS, THOMAS S.: 1932. "Birds of Minnesota," Univ. of Minn. Press, Minneapolis.

SAUNDERS, ARETAS A.: 1929. "Bird Song," N. Y. State Museum, Albany.

SCHMITT, CORNEL, and STADLER, HANS: 1919. "die Vogelsprache," Stuttgart.

SCOTT, W. E. D.: 1904. "The Inheritance of Song in Passerine Birds," *Science*, New Series, vols. 19, 20.

SUTTON, GEO. MIKOSCH: 1928. "Birds of Pennsylvania," J. H. McFarland, Harrisburg, Pa.

VOIGT, A.: 1929. "Excursionbuch zum Studium der Vogelstimmen," Leipsic.

WITCHELL, CHARLES A.: 1896. "The Evolution of Bird Song," A. & C. Black, London.

INDEX OF COMMON NAMES